HEALTH
and
SOCIAL CARE

FOR FOUNDATION GNVQ

Alan Skelt and Beryl Stretch

Hodder & Stoughton

A MEMBER OF THE HODDER HEADLINE GROUP

Cataloguing in Publication Data is available from the British Library

ISBN 0 340 621117

First published 1995
Impression number 10 9 8 7 6 5 4 3 2 1
Year   1999 1998 1997 1996 1995

Typeset by Wearset, Boldon, Tyne and Wear.
Printed in Great Britain for Hodder & Stoughton Educational, a division of Hodder Headline Plc, 338 Euston Road, London NW1 3BH by The Bath Press, Avon

HEALTH AND SOCIAL CARE FOR FOUNDATION GNVQ

How to use this book

Health and Social Care for Foundation GNVQ will help you prepare for this, your first GNVQ course. Each chapter has been written to cover one of the units of the course.

The first three chapters are for each of the three mandatory units, which you must take, and for which there is a test. These chapters include plenty of self-test questions, so that you can keep track of your learning as you proceed through the unit. By the time you take the test, you can be confident that you know *all* you need to know! There are also many activities, which are designed to help you gather and present the information you need for your portfolio of evidence.

The next six chapters cover the major option units of the Foundation course. You must take three of these, and will probably be told as a group which three these will be. Again there are self-test questions to check your own progress (though no test to pass!) and activities to help build your portfolio of evidence.

The activities are designed especially to develop your *core skills*. It will be important to keep a record of the core skills you have used, as you will also need to present this record in your portfolio.

The questions and activities are highlighted with icons:

 Student activity

 Self-check questions

There are other symbols throughout the book which will draw your attention to key points and useful information.

The Foundation course is designed to lead you into the field of Health and Social Care, so that you can gradually build up your knowledge and abilities in the field. In the same way, this book increases its depth and coverage as it progresses, so that some of the later chapters will develop and extend your skills far more than the earlier ones.

ACKNOWLEDGEMENTS

The publishers would like to thank the following contributors for the permission to reproduce copyright material: fig 2, Kellogg Company; fig 3, Brian Shuel/Collections; figs 6, 13, 16–18, Anthea Sieveking/ Collections; fig 11, John & Eliza Forder/ Collections; fig 12 Nancy Durrell McKenna/ The Hutchinson Library; fig 15, Nancy Fyson/J. Allan Cash Ltd; figs 19, 23, 24, Sam Tanner/Photofusion; figs 20, 21, 47, David Montford/Photofusion; fig 25, Townly Cooke/photofusion; figs 28, 30, Comstock Photofile Ltd; fig 34, Emma Lee/Life File; fig 44, Pete Jenkins/J. Allan Cash Ltd; fig 46, Michael McIntyre/The Hutchinson Library; fig 49, J. Allan Cash Ltd.

Every effort has been made to trace copyright holders of material reproduced in this book. Any rights not acknowledged here will be acknowledged in subsequent printings if notice is given to the publisher.

CONTENTS

Health and Social Care for Foundation GNVQ　　　　　　　　*iii*

Acknowledgements　　　　　　　　*iv*

Chapter 1 Understanding health and well-being　　　　　　　　**1**

Element 1.1 Plan how to improve health and well-being　　　　　1
 Student activity 1　　　　　1
 Diet　　　　　1
 Self-check questions　　　　　2
 Student activity 2　　　　　3
 Student activity 3　　　　　3
 Student activity 4　　　　　3
 Keeping fit in mind and body　　　　　5
 Student activity 5　　　　　5
 Student activity 6　　　　　5
 Student activity 7　　　　　6

Element 1.2 Investigate risks to health　　　　　7
 Keeping healthy　　　　　7
 Basic health needs　　　　　8
 Student activity 8　　　　　8
 Client groups　　　　　8
 Student activity 9　　　　　9
 Self-check questions　　　　　9
 Social settings　　　　　9
 Stressful situations　　　　　10
 Student acitivity 10　　　　　10
 Self-check questions　　　　　10
 Effects of stress　　　　　10
 Student activity 11　　　　　11
 What can be done about stress?　　　　　11
 Self-check questions　　　　　13

Chapter 2 Understanding personal development and relationships　　　　　　　　**14**

Element 2.1 Investigate personal development　　　　　14
 Life stages　　　　　14
 Self-check questions　　　　　15
 Student activity 1　　　　　19

CONTENTS

Self-check questions 19
Student activity 2 21
Social factors influencing personal development 22
Self-check question 23
Student activity 3 24
Self-check questions 26
Student activity 4 27
Self-check questions 27
Student activity 5 28
Self-check questions 28
Student activity 6 29
Self-check questions 29
Student activity 7 29
Student activity 8 30

Element 2.2 Explore relationships at different life stages 30
Relationships 31
Self-check questions 31
Student activity 9 32
Self-check questions 33
Student activity 10 36

Element 2.3 Explore relationships between clients and carers 36
Clients 37
Carers 37
Student activity 11 38
Student activity 12 39
Barriers to forming effective relationships 41
Student activity 13 42
Self-check questions 42

Chapter 3 Investigating working in health and social care 43

Element 3.1 Working in UK health and social care services 43
Health care and social care 43
Student activity 1 43
Welfare state 43
Self-check questions 44
Student activity 2 45
Self-check questions 46
Student activity 3 46
Self-check questions 49
Self-check questions 50
Student activity 4 (role play) 51
Self-check questions 51
Student activity 5 52
Hospitals 52
Student activity 6 52

CONTENTS

Social care	53
Self-check questions	54
Student activity 7	54
Element 3.2 Investigate jobs in health and social care	56
Choosing a job	56
Student activity 8	56
Student activity 9	56
Element 3.3 Plan for employment in health and social care	57
Curriculum vitae	58
Student activity 10	58
Student activity 11	59
Finding jobs	63
Student activity 12	66
Self-check questions	67
Chapter 4 Contributing to a team activity	**69**
Element 4.1 Plan an activity with a team	70
Ideas for activities	71
Suggested team activity	75
Student activity 1	75
Element 4.2 Undertake a role in a team activity	76
Evidence	76
Element 4.3 Review the activity	77
Self-check questions	77
Team-check questions	78
Student activity 2	78
Chapter 5 Investigating common health emergencies	**79**
Element 5.1 Investigate key health and safety factors in care settings	79
Common hazards and ways of reducing risks	79
Student activity 1	80
Student activity 2	81
Student activity 3	82
Student activity 4	82
Student activity 5	82
Student activity 6	83
Student activity 7	84
Student activity 8	86
Student activity 9	86
Safety precautions and safe working practices	87
Student activity 10	88
Health and safety regulations	88

CONTENTS

Student activity 11	89
Student activity 12	89
Self-check questions	90

Element 5.2 Explore common health emergencies — 90

Element 5.3 Investigate emergency care procedures — 90
Asthma	91
Student activity 13	92
Student activity 14	92
Epileptic fit	93
Concussion	94
Recovery position	94
Burns and scalds	95
Cuts	97
Electric shock	97
Choking	98
Poisoning	99
Heart attack	99
Broken bones	100
Resuscitation	101
Student activity 15	102
Student activity 16	102
Student activity 17	103
Self-check questions	104

Chapter 6 Planning diets — 105

Element 6.1 Exploring the main features of a healthy diet — 105
Main nutrients	105
Student activity 1	107
Student activity 2	107
Student activity 3	108
Student activity 4	110
Student activity 5	111

Element 6.2 Investigate balanced diets for clients with different needs — 112
Nutritional needs of different client groups	113
Student activity 6	113
What influences food habits?	115
What influences our choice of food?	115
Student activity 7	115
Student activity 8	117

Element 6.3 Plan and cost diets — 117
Student activity 9	120

CONTENTS

Chapter 7 Exploring health and recreational activities ⟶ 123

Element 7.1 Investigate health and recreational activities ⟶ 123
Student activity 1 ⟶ 124
Student activity 2 ⟶ 126
Student activity 3 ⟶ 127

Element 7.2 Survey the use of local recreational activities ⟶ 127
Student activity 4 ⟶ 128
Barriers ⟶ 129
Student activity 5 ⟶ 130

Element 7.3 Suggest recreational activities for clients with specific needs ⟶ 130
Clients with physical disabilities ⟶ 131
Clients with a problem of obesity ⟶ 131
Clients who are elderly ⟶ 132
Student activity 6 ⟶ 133
Student activity 7 ⟶ 134
Why should clients bother with recreational activities? ⟶ 134
Student activity 8 ⟶ 135
Health and safety factors ⟶ 135
Student activity 9 ⟶ 136

Chapter 8 Exploring physical care ⟶ 137

Element 8.1 Investigate the provision of physical assistance ⟶ 137
Clients who might require physical help ⟶ 137
Student activity 1 ⟶ 140
Cooking ⟶ 140
Feeding ⟶ 141
Student activity 2 ⟶ 142
Dressing ⟶ 142
Bathing ⟶ 142
Safe lifting techniques ⟶ 143
Student activity 3 ⟶ 145
Maintaining client independence and dignity ⟶ 145
Student activity 4 ⟶ 147
Student activity 5 ⟶ 147

Element 8.2 Investigate the use of physical care aids ⟶ 147
Main types of aids ⟶ 147
Ways of operating the aids ⟶ 151
Health and safety factors ⟶ 151
Constraints ⟶ 151
Student activity 6 ⟶ 151

Element 8.3 Investigate how aids help maintain independence ⟶ 152
Sources of physical care aids ⟶ 152

Support networks for clients using physical care aids   153
Student activity 7   154

Chapter 9 Investigating health and care service provision   **155**

Element 9.1 Investigate the organisation of health and care services   155
Organisation of the National Health Service   155
Student activity 1   155
Social services   156
Voluntary organisations   157
Student activity 2   157
Private organisations   158

Element 9.2 Investigate access to health and care services   158
Local needs   158
Student activity 3   159
Methods of referral   159
Student activity 4   160
Restrictions   160
Student activity 5   160
Student activity 6   161
Student activity 7   161
Student activity 8   162
Evidence indicators   162
Student activity 9   162

Element 9.3 Investigate communicating information in health and social care   162
Sources of information   163
Ways of publicising   164
Student activity 10   164
Student activity 11   166

Appendix: Answers to questions   **167**

1

UNDERSTANDING HEALTH AND WELL-BEING (FOUNDATION)

Plan how to improve health and well-being

If you are thinking of a job which involves looking after people, it is important to know how to keep them as fit, safe and as well as possible. It is important that you are as physically and mentally healthy as possible so that you can help to the best of your ability. This unit will give you advice on how to do both of these things.

The first part of the unit is about improving health and well-being. At the end of the work for this element, you should have evidence for your portfolio which

- describes the main factors contributing to good health and well-being
- identifies reasons for improving your own health and well-being
- suggests ways to improve your own health and well-being
- provides a clearly presented plan for improving your own health and well-being.

Student activity 1

To help keep a record of information you need for this unit, make an element diary to cover at least seven days. Seven pages from your A4 writing pad should be enough. Write the day you are starting and the date, on the top of the first page, and the next day and date on the next page until you have enough for a week. You will need the diary to record what you eat and drink, and what activities you have done.

What you should record in it will be found in the student activity sections.

DIET

This is the word used for all the things we eat and drink. When people talk about 'dieting' or being on a 'special diet', they mean that they are taking care about what they eat, choosing their food and drinks carefully. It helps them to make sure they have all the nutrients the body needs, or to avoid anything which may cause harm or disagree with them.

People who are slimming will try to avoid any foods or drinks with a lot of sugar or fats in them, and people who are pregnant will want to get as much iron and as many vitamins into their diet as possible.

If you are eating normally, it is not necessary to do more than make sure you are getting a good mix of foods to make up a 'balanced diet'. If you want to eat chocolate or have fizzy drinks, this is fine – in moderation, and as part of an overall healthy diet. The more you eat different kinds of food, the more chance you have of getting some of everything you need to be healthy.

So what do we need for a balanced healthy diet?

- **protein** comes from eating meat, fish, cheese and eggs, as well as peas, beans, lentils and nuts
- **fats** from butter, margarine, milk, cheese, fat in meat, and cooking oils
- **carbohydrates** from bread, pasta, rice and cereals
- **fibre**, which is found in fruit and vegetables as well as some breakfast cereals
- **vitamins and minerals**, from vegetables, meat and dairy products

If you are eating a balanced diet, some foods from each section in the correct proportions should be included every day. All the main supermarkets have free leaflets and booklets available which give advice on healthy eating. You can also get information from the Health Education Authority, or the Health Education Unit of your local Health Trust. Their number and address will be in your local 'phone book.

There is often useful information on food packaging. The questionnaire shown in Figure 2 was recently featured on Kelloggs All-Bran boxes.

Should we be worried?

By the time we are adults most of us will suffer some form of disease due to our diet. We only have to look in our mouths to see fillings resulting from tooth decay. A trivial disease, perhaps, but dental services cost the National Health Service (NHS) over £450 million every year.

If we could look at our hearts and arteries and see their condition we might be more alarmed. Heart disease kills a quarter of us, and what we eat contributes greatly to these deaths. Worse still, the age at which heart disease occurs is decreasing – people in their 30s and 40s are having heart attacks in increasing numbers.

Cancer, too, is related to diet. A report from the World Health Organisation estimated that about 40% of cancers in men, and a remarkable 60% in women were linked to diets that had too much fatty food – especially animal fats – and not enough vegetables and fruit. Apart from the links between smoking and lung cancer, diet was the main cause of cancer, especially of the mouth, stomach and bowel, as well as of the breast and womb.

Piles (haemorrhoids) and various other bowel diseases occurring in later life are often the result of a lifetime of eating low-fibre food.

Other diseases are related to eating too much and becoming overweight.

From cancer to coronaries, cancer to constipation, diet is being recognised as a major factor in our general health.

(Whiting and Lobstein, 1994)

Self-check questions

 1 What will most of us have suffered by the time we are adults?

2 How much do dental services cost each year?

Figure 1   *Make sure you are getting a variety of foods to achieve a balanced diet*

3 How many of us does heart disease kill?
4 What is happening to the age at which heart disease occurs?
5 What is cancer related to?
6 What % of cancers in women are linked to too much fatty food?
7 What is strongly linked with lung cancer?
8 What is often the result of eating low-fibre food?

Student activity 2

Starting from today, make a list in your element diary of everything you eat and drink, and how much, for a full seven days. Start with breakfast, include snacks between meals, and anything at all which you eat or drink until you go to bed. If you have a snack in bed, then that should also be on the list. A new day starts at midnight.

Student activity 3

Make a list of your favourite foods. Next to them, write which of the four types of food they contain (carbohydrate, fat, fibre or protein).

Student activity 4

At the end of the seven days, you should have in your element diary a list of everything you have eaten and drunk.

How much fibre do you eat?

Most people know fibre is important but, despite this, research shows that nine out of every ten people are still not eating enough fibre—are you?

QUESTIONNAIRE

To help you find out how much fibre you eat, Kellogg's has obtained a simple self-analysed questionnaire. Devised and tested by the University of Birmingham Department of Social Medicine, the questionnaire will enable you to analyse your diet for fibre intake. It's simple to fill in and there are no right or wrong answers, so be honest with yourself!

HOW TO COMPLETE

Answer each question. Tick the box nearest to your answer, e.g. Question 1, if your answer is D—tick score 20.

1 What kind of breakfast cereal do you regularly eat?

	SCORE
A. All Bran, other high fibre cereal	A. 100
B. Puffed wheat, bran flakes, wheat biscuits, shredded wheat, wheat flakes, other whole wheat cereal, oat bran flakes	B. 50 / C. 50
C. Muesli	D. 20
D. Corn flakes, Rice Krispies, other cereal	E. 0
E. Don't eat breakfast cereal	

2 On a typical weekday, how many slices of bread do you eat? (a roll counts as two slices of bread)

	SCORE
A. None	A. 0
B. 1–2	B. 28
C. 3–5	C. 56
D. 6 or more	D. 84

3 What sort of bread do you usually eat?

	SCORE
A. Wholemeal	A. 20
B. Brown (not wholemeal)	B. 7
C. White	C. 5
D. Mixture of bread types	D. 7
E. None	E. 0

4 On a typical weekday, how many biscuits would you eat?

	SCORE
A. 5 or more	A. 6
B. 3 or 4	B. 4
C. 1 or 2	C. 2
D. Only eat biscuits once or twice in a week	D. 1
E. Rarely or never eat biscuits	E. 0

The following answers refer to questions 5–22

How many times a week do you eat these foods?

A. Twice or more a day F. Once a week
B. Once a day G. Once a fortnight
C. 5–6 times a week H. Less than once a fortnight
D. 3–4 times a week
E. Twice a week

5 Baked beans:

	SCORE		SCORE		SCORE		SCORE
A.	140	B.	70	C.	50	D.	30
E.	20	F.	10	G.	5	H.	0

6 Breakfast cereal:

	SCORE		SCORE		SCORE		SCORE
A.	112	B.	56	C.	40	D.	24
E.	16	F.	8	G.	4	H.	0

7 Fresh fruit:

	SCORE		SCORE		SCORE		SCORE
A.	70	B.	35	C.	25	D.	15
E.	10	F.	5	G.	3	H.	0

8 Tinned fruit:

	SCORE		SCORE		SCORE		SCORE
A.	70	B.	35	C.	25	D.	15
E.	10	F.	5	G.	3	H.	0

9 Dried fruit:

	SCORE		SCORE		SCORE		SCORE
A.	70	B.	35	C.	25	D.	15
E.	10	F.	5	G.	3	H.	0

10 Leafy vegetables, e.g. cabbage:

	SCORE		SCORE		SCORE		SCORE
A.	42	B.	21	C.	15	D.	9
E.	6	F.	3	G.	2	H.	0

11 Root vegetables, e.g. carrots:

	SCORE		SCORE		SCORE		SCORE
A.	42	B.	21	C.	15	D.	9
E.	6	F.	3	G.	2	H.	0

12 Jacket potatoes:

	SCORE		SCORE		SCORE		SCORE
A.	28	B.	14	C.	10	D.	6
E.	4	F.	2	G.	1	H.	0

13 Boiled potatoes:

	SCORE		SCORE		SCORE		SCORE
A.	28	B.	14	C.	10	D.	6
E.	4	F.	2	G.	1	H.	0

14 Mashed potatoes:

	SCORE		SCORE		SCORE		SCORE
A.	28	B.	14	C.	10	D.	6
E.	4	F.	2	G.	1	H.	0

15 Roast potatoes:

	SCORE		SCORE		SCORE		SCORE
A.	28	B.	14	C.	10	D.	6
E.	4	F.	2	G.	1	H.	0

16 Chips:

	SCORE		SCORE		SCORE		SCORE
A.	28	B.	14	C.	10	D.	6
E.	4	F.	2	G.	1	H.	0

17 Biscuits:

	SCORE		SCORE		SCORE		SCORE
A.	28	B.	14	C.	10	D.	6
E.	4	F.	2	G.	1	H.	0

18 Rice:

	SCORE		SCORE		SCORE		SCORE
A.	14	B.	7	C.	5	D.	3
E.	2	F.	1	G.	1	H.	0

19 Pasta:

	SCORE		SCORE		SCORE		SCORE
A.	14	B.	7	C.	5	D.	3
E.	2	F.	1	G.	1	H.	0

20 Crispbreads:

	SCORE		SCORE		SCORE		SCORE
A.	14	B.	7	C.	5	D.	3
E.	2	F.	1	G.	1	H.	0

21 Crisps:

	SCORE		SCORE		SCORE		SCORE
A.	14	B.	7	C.	5	D.	3
E.	2	F.	1	G.	1	H.	0

22 Salads:

	SCORE		SCORE		SCORE		SCORE
A.	14	B.	7	C.	5	D.	3
E.	2	F.	1	G.	1	H.	0

THE ANALYSIS

Now add up all the scores you ticked and your total score will provide you with an indication of your fibre intake.

If it is:

Less than 170—your fibre intake is low and you are most likely to benefit by eating more fibre-rich foods.

Between 171 and 230—you are on the border line and you may wish to consider including a few more high-fibre foods in your daily diet.

Over 231—Well done, your fibre intake is adequate and meets the recommendations set by health experts. You should be enjoying all the benefits of a fibre-rich diet. Keep it up!

Kellogg's
ALL-BRAN

Figure 2 *Useful information on packaging*

- Was it a balanced diet? Draw four columns on a piece of paper, and have one column for each food type (fat, fibre, protein and carbohydrate). List in the columns which of the foods fits in which category.
- If you have a kilojoule counter, you can work out how many kilojoules you took in each day.
- Now that you have worked out what your diet was, what changes do you need to make for it to be healthy and balanced?
- Plan a diet for one week using the information about what you have eaten, and the new information about what you should be eating in order to stay healthy. Keep this for your evidence portfolio.

KEEPING FIT IN MIND AND BODY

Keeping healthy is not just a matter of eating a balanced diet. There are a number of other things involved, such as getting enough sleep, not smoking, and not taking illegal drugs. Exercise is also very important, and so is taking part in other recreational activities or hobbies which are a complete change from studying and work.

Student activity 5

- Spend a few minutes making a list of what you do with your time when you are not at school or college. Do you play computer games, watch television, read books, play football, go ice skating, walk in the park, swim or go birdwatching?

You could do this using two columns, one for active, and one for non-active pastimes, e.g.

Active	Non-active
Swimming	Reading
Playing football	Watching television

- Write down anything you do, either by yourself or with other people.
- Using your element diary, keep a record of all the things which you have done for a week. Which of them made you the most out of breath?
- Which exercise was the most tiring?
- How did your body tell you this?
- Take your pulse before you do any exercise, and write down the number of beats per minute you counted.
- Do something energetic, such as dancing for five minutes, or riding a bike, and then take your pulse again.
- Is it different from the first time you took it?
- Why is this?

In order to keep fit, you should do something energetic at least three times a week, and for at least 20 minutes each time. Exercise helps to improve your strength, suppleness (being able to move and bend more easily) and stamina (staying power). You should only do exercise you are able to do safely.

Older people will not be able to do all the things that teenagers do, for example, and young children or disabled people should have exercises designed to meet their needs. There are plenty of wheelchair sports, though, including basketball and rugby.

Student activity 6

- Where do the people who live in your area go for their exercise? Either draw a map, or mark on a printed map, the places you have found (see Figure 4). For example, the park, leisure centre, skating rink and swimming pool.

Non-active pastimes also have benefits for the people taking part in them. It may be something as simple as stopping them

Figure 3   *There are plenty of ways to keep fit*

becoming bored, but it may also help them learn new things, or bring them into contact with other people.

Student activity 7

- What do you get out of the leisure pastimes you take part in, both active and non-active?
- Having looked at your activities in the element diary, what could you do to improve things? Do you need more exercise? Do you need to get out and meet more people? Is there anything you could do differently – is there something you do by yourself which could easily be shared with somebody else?

Write an action plan of what you are going to do for the next week. Include the reason you will be doing those things, and if there are any changes you are making as a result of what you have learned on this course.

Explain why you are making any changes that you make. Keep all this written work for your portfolio.

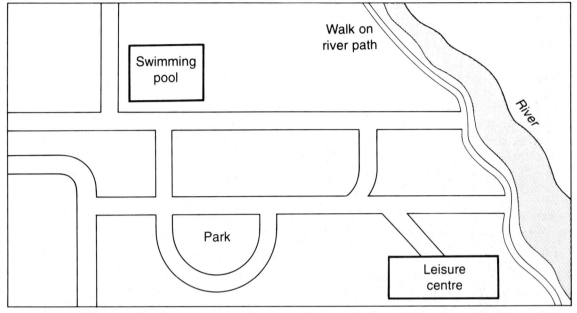

Figure 4   *A simple town map showing leisure facilities*

ELEMENT 1.2

Investigate risks to health

At the end of this section, you should have

- described the basic health needs of individuals
- identified and given examples of the basic health needs of the main client groups
- identified the main risks to the health and well-being of the main client groups for different social settings
- described how best to reduce the risks to health and well-being and given examples
- described the effects of major changes in circumstances on health and well-being
- described ways of coping with major changes in circumstances

KEEPING HEALTHY

Eating a balanced diet and taking exercise at least three times a week, as mentioned in Element 1.1, are not enough by themselves to keep you healthy. As well as things that you should do, there are things that are better not to do. One of the main things not to do is smoke. If you do smoke, the best thing you can do to improve your health is to stop. Even if you do not have a balanced diet and take no exercise, stopping smoking will go a long way to improving your health.

Another thing to avoid is drinking too much alcohol.

It is also not a good idea to take drugs not

prescribed for you by your doctor – or take more than the doctor says you should.

You should avoid having sex without using a condom. Condoms help protect you against sexually transmitted diseases, as well as being one method of avoiding pregnancy.

Poor personal hygiene is something which may not seem all that important, except if your friends think that you smell. But not keeping yourself properly clean can give you skin diseases, mouth problems, and infestations such as scabies and lice.

Being clean and tidy is even more important if you are caring for other people, as you often have to get very close to them – to lift them up or feed them, for instance. Not very nice for them if you have smelly armpits or bad breath, is it? Advice on dental care is available at any dentist.

BASIC HEALTH NEEDS

The basic health needs of all of us can be put into four groups

- Physical
- Intellectual
- Emotional
- Social

You can remember these as **PIES**, as in apple pies.

Our physical needs are such things as air to breathe, water to drink and food to eat plus clothes to keep us warm. It also includes the need to take exercise and keep active.

Intellectual needs are those which give the mind some exercise, such as watching a film, reading a book or going to the theatre.

Emotional needs are knowing that we are wanted, belong to a group such as a family; having confidence in yourself, and knowing that you are loved by other people.

Social needs are those of friendship, having outside interests, time to relax, and generally doing things you enjoy with other people.

Student activity 8

 Using PIES, make a list under each heading of the things you do which meet those needs. Some of the things may come under more than one heading, e.g. going to a disco with friends (see below).
Can you add anything to that list which you would like to do, and which would improve your health and sense of well-being?

CLIENT GROUPS

Some of the main client groups which people look after when working in caring are

- infants (from birth to one year old)
- children (from one to ten years old)
- adolescents (from eleven to eighteen years old)

Physical	Intellectual	Emotional	Social
Eating	Reading	Disco with friends	Disco with friends

- adults (from eighteen years old onwards)
- elders (or 'older people', from age 65 onwards).

Each of these groups will have different needs.

A baby will not need the same things as an adolescent for instance, and an older person will probably have different needs to a 30-year-old.

Student activity 9

 Using other books (from the college or school library, or your local library) make a PIES list for each of the groups above. It may help to speak to a person from each group, or their parent in the case of infants and children, to see what they need. Or you could speak to someone who works in a care setting looking after people. You can also use yourself for the age group that you fit into, and write down what you need.

Self-check questions

1 What is the least number of times you should be taking exercise each week?
2 What is one of the main things not to do if you want to stay healthy?
3 Name two other things you should avoid doing in order to stay healthy.
4 What do condoms prevent?
5 Why is it important to keep yourself clean, especially if you are looking after other people?
6 What do the letters PIES stand for?
7 Give one example of a need from each (P, I, E, and S).
8 Name three of the main client groups.

SOCIAL SETTINGS

People's needs differ in different settings. For those who cannot leave their own house, the risks are different to those who can get out and about.

Somebody confined to a house or flat will have trouble with a proper diet unless there is somebody who can shop for them. The client group most likely to be in this situation are older people, or people with disabilities. They may also need somebody to come in and cook and clean for them. They may also need help to keep themselves clean.

Exercise could be another problem. Sitting in a chair all day or lying in a bed does not use the muscles very much. Some people in this situation may also smoke or drink alcohol to try to cheer themselves up. Others will eat 'comfort foods' like chocolates, cream cakes and biscuits. The risks then become very high. Sitting or lying still; not getting a varied diet; smoking and drinking. Putting weight on is one of the things which could easily happen. If we are too heavy, it affects our heart. Not getting exercise and smoking affects our lungs.

Even people who are being looked after in care settings such as hostels or retirement homes can be at risk. A close watch has to be kept to check that they are eating the meals given to them, and that too much alcohol is not brought in. Eating comfort foods instead of meals is also a risk, and smoking is a fire risk as well as a health risk in places where it is necessary to oversee a lot of people at once. Efforts should also be made to see that residents get some sort of exercise, even if it is while sitting in an armchair.

STRESSFUL SITUATIONS

There are other risks to health in addition to those we have looked at already. There are some things which give us real worry, and can make you feel very 'stressed up'.

You probably know what it is like to feel stress, but different people worry about different things, so we do not all become stressed at the same time about the same things.

How do you feel when you have to take exams? Or when you did something wrong at school and got into trouble for it? What does it feel like sitting in the dentist's waiting room listening to other people having their teeth drilled when your turn is coming next?

Other situations which may cause you stress are going for a driving test, starting school, moving to a new school or college, or having a really bad argument.

Student activity 10

- Write down what you feel like in any stressful situation such as the ones above.
- What is happening to your body when you are stressed? Does your breathing stay the same? Are you sweating? Do you notice any other changes?
- When you have written this down for yourself, ask another person in the group what they have put down, and tell them what you wrote. Do you both feel the same kind of things? What about the other people in the group, do they feel similar things when they are stressed?

Some of these stressful situations only last for a short time, and are not really serious.

Going to the dentist, or taking a driving test or another sort of exam is soon over with. Other life risks last a long time, and are difficult to get over. Moving house is said to be one of the most stressful things that anybody can do. This obviously depends on how many people are involved, and how long you have lived in one place.

A single teenager living in college lodgings or a bedsit will not really suffer much stress packing a couple of bin-bags and moving somewhere else. Parents with young children who have lived in one house for ten years will have much more stress to deal with.

Other bad times in life are divorce, being made redundant, the death of somebody close to you, major illnesses, and not being able to find a job.

Self-check questions

1 Can you remember ever having to move house?

2 What was it like?

EFFECTS OF STRESS

You will have written down some of the effects of stress in the exercise above where you wrote about how you feel in a stressful situation. The short-term effects include breathing too fast, butterflies in the stomach, dry mouth, cold sweats and the heart beating very fast.

The longer term effects might include feeling tired and bad-tempered all the time; having a string of minor illnesses; headaches, and chest pains; losing weight or gaining weight. Some people stop eating under stress, others eat more, and of the wrong kinds of food such as cream cakes and chocolate.

The way that stress affects people is very individual, and easier to recognise than to explain. When we are under stress, the body releases 'stress chemicals', including adrenaline. This causes the symptoms already mentioned (butterflies, sweating, shaking, needing the toilet). In the days when we were cavemen and hunting wild animals for food, the adrenaline got us ready to run away or to fight – the 'fight or flight response'.

It is no good trying to run away from or fight the causes of most of our stress in today's world, though. Running away from the bills or fighting with the driver in front in a traffic jam doesn't help anybody.

The stress chemicals need to be used up when they have been produced. If they are not used up, they stay in the body and cause long-lasting problems such as indigestion, chest pains, and skin disorders like psoriasis.

Student activity 11

You can get some practice in recognising stress and the symptoms with this exercise.

- Each person in the group should think of the worst moment they can remember. Write down a few words to remind you of what it was like, then stand up and tell everyone else about it.
- Call it 'my worst moment', and the only thing you should not talk about is standing up and giving the talk now – even if it does feel like your worst moment!

WHAT CAN BE DONE ABOUT STRESS?

One way to get rid of the stress chemicals quickly is to have a good shout and scream – arguments often do that without you realising it. Sometimes they just make things worse, though. Another way is to do something energetic like housework, digging, or going for a run.

Planning ahead is the best way to avoid stress. If you are going out anywhere, even to college, allow yourself plenty of time to get ready and pack whatever you need to take with you. Stop getting up at the last minute and running for the bus or train. When you are going on holiday, make a list of what you need weeks in advance, and get ready slowly. Pack your case the day before, and then check it to make sure you haven't forgotten anything. This should keep any stress to a very low level. If you are going to make a meal, check that you have all you need before the shops close. If you need to buy anything, do so in time to cook it.

One thing at a time. Don't try to do too many things at once. Finish one thing before you start another. It is not a good idea to go home and do your homework at the same time as you are cooking a meal or cleaning your room.

Hobbies and pastimes are very good at releasing tension and stress. It is always good to have something to do which interests you and is not work; so dancing, exercises, playing football or train-spotting all have a part to play.

Figure 5   *Relaxation helps reduce stress*

Relaxation is a method used to help people feel less stressed. The first thing that has to be done is to create a restful feeling. So a darkened, quiet room at a comfortable temperature is a good place to start. Soft carpets and comfortable furniture are also a great help.

Relaxation is used with pregnant women, and by psychologists and psychiatrists to help people with anxiety problems. There are also many pre-recorded tapes available for people to use to relax at home.

When you are in the right situation, either at home lying on a bed, or with a group of people lying on the floor of your warm, darkened room, put on some soft music or background sound. Some of the tapes have beach noises – the sea and sea-birds. Others have countryside noises of birds singing and trees rustling in the wind. Others just have soft, gentle music.

The session is started by asking everyone to lie down or relax in a comfortable chair; then to clear their minds of all their worries, and concentrate on the background music or sounds. Then starting at the top of the body (the face and head), to tense the muscles for a few seconds and then relax.

So you would start with 'clench your jaw; hold for a count of five. Relax, and breathe out'. Always use a soft voice, speaking slowly to help with the relaxed atmosphere. Then 'screw up your face, hold, relax'. Then the shoulders, stomach, hands, arms, bottom, legs and down to the feet. Tensing, holding and relaxing each set of muscles in turn. Do this slowly, and when you have finished just lie there for ten minutes or so with the soft music or background sounds playing. Then slowly sit up and get back to the rest of the day. The whole session should take about 20 to 30 minutes each time, and once or twice a day should be enough to help reduce stress in most people.

Self-check questions

1 What is one of the most stressful things that people can do?
2 Identify two bad times in life when stress might become a problem.
3 Write down three effects of stress on the body.
4 What causes the 'fight or flight' response?
5 Name two ways to get rid of stress chemicals.
6 Identify two ways of avoiding stress.

Remember to record evidence for your portfolio.

Reference
Whiting, M. and Lobstein T. (1994) *The Nursery Food Book*, London: Edward Arnold.

2

UNDERSTANDING PERSONAL DEVELOPMENT AND RELATIONSHIPS

Investigate personal development

At the end of this chapter you should be able to:

- identify when the main life stages occur in personal development
- describe the main characteristics of each main life stage of personal development
- describe the social factors which influence personal development

- describe the economic factors which influence personal development
- identify the economic and social factors influencing your own personal development

LIFE STAGES

After we are born, we do not grow up all at once. We start off as a baby, and mature over the next 70 years or so to become an elder. In between we go through a number of 'stages', which are called 'life stages'.

Infancy

This is the earliest stage, and lasts from birth until about one year. Our first stage of independent development is when we are babies. We are unable to survive alone in the world, and need somebody there to look after us, and make sure that all our needs are met.

Babies need frequent feeding and changing. The mother is usually the main carer, but not in every case. Premature babies (those who are born before the normal nine months of pregnancy are completed) rely on nurses, doctors and machines to keep them alive.

Sometimes the mother is too ill to care for a child, or she has died. In these cases, somebody else has to take over looking after the baby. Sometimes mothers pay for other people to look after their children, such as a nanny or a childminder.

Babies carry on growing and developing quickly after birth. *Growth* means to increase in size, *development* means increasing abilities, but they are closely linked. A baby won't develop enough to hold on to anything until the hands have grown enough to grip things, for instance.

There are certain 'milestones' a baby

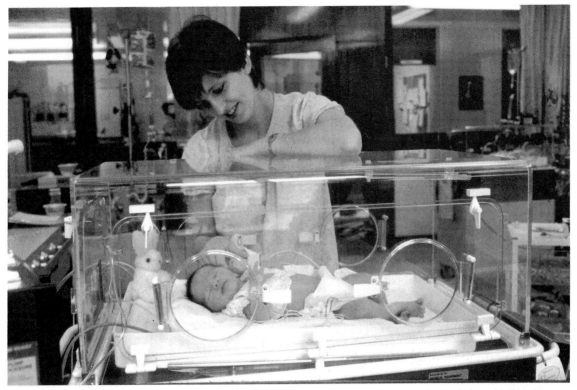

Figure 6   *Premature babies need extra care*

reaches as it is growing up. These are not reached at the same time by each child, but almost always they are reached in the same order, such as being able to walk, or to talk. There is an average age when things are expected to happen, and this causes problems with some parents who expect the changes and are very worried when their baby cannot do the things that are suggested may happen at the given time.

Self-check questions

 Using Table 2.1.1, write down your answers to the following questions.

At what age may a child

1 Recognise mother?
2 Use 200 or more words?
3 Put their own shoes on?
4 Sleep for 20 hours a day?
5 Enjoy looking at picture books?
6 Not wet the bed for a whole night?
7 Say a few words?
8 Start to have temper tantrums?
9 Put everything in his/her mouth?
10 Be able to build a tower from wooden blocks?

See Appendix for answers.

Age	Physical development	Intellectual development
One month	Eyes follow moving objects, especially bright ones Able to hold head erect for a few seconds at a time	Likes gentle noises
Three months	Kicks strongly Eyes follow people around	Recognises faces seen regularly Responds to people by smiling or with excited movements
Six months	Can lift head and upper body with help (e.g. by parent holding wrists) Turns toward noises	Pays attention to noises Explores everything that can be touched Babbles
Nine months	Can stand up with support Will look at self in mirror May sit up May try to drink from a cup	Tries to talk, and may say 'mama' or 'dada' Shouts to get attention Knows the meaning of 'no'
One year	Can stand up using furniture as a support May start to walk a few steps Can grip with finger and thumb Can point to things	Responds to name, and follows simple instructions Can say a few words
Eighteen months	Can walk, including up stairs, and is starting to run Likes to push and pull big toys	Uses about 20 words, and can repeat many more Enjoys looking at picture books Can build a small tower of wooden blocks Can hold crayons and make scribbles with them, and shows whether s/he will be left or right handed
Two years	Runs about; climbs on furniture Throws things Can ride a tricycle	Uses more than 50 words, and can use them in simple sentences Asks what things are called Uses own name
Two and a half years	Controls all body movements Runs, climbs, jumps off low objects, and can kick a ball about	Uses 200–300 words Likes to listen to stories, especially with pictures
Three years	Walks upstairs putting one foot on each step May sit with feet crossed at the ankles	Can hold simple conversations, but is always asking questions Knows name, age, and whether they are a boy or a gi Is learning to count, and knows some colours Can copy simple shapes such as a circle or a cross

Table 2.1.1   *Developmental milestones*

Emotional development	Social development
Cries when hungry, thirsty, or in pain	Sleeps up to 20 hours a day Cries, but stops when given attention such as being spoken to or picked up
Likes a lot of attention, cuddling, tickling and so on Cries when this stops	Responds to carer's presence Gets excited when going to have a bath or a feed
May show anger May show fear of strange faces	Plays with fingers and toes Tries to get hold of feeding bottle Puts everything in mouth
Recognises individuals seen regularly, e.g. mother, father, brothers or sisters Likes a routine to be kept (for feeding, sleeping, playing, etc.)	Tries to imitate hand actions such as clapping
Returns kisses and cuddles Less afraid of strange faces	Can drink from a cup without help Can hold a spoon or fork Finds hidden toys
No major changes from one year	Can use a spoon to get food to mouth (messily) Takes off shoes and socks Has learned some bowel control Hands objects back to carer
Likes a lot of attention from mother or carer Has temper tantrums if not getting own way Plays beside other children but not with them	Will ask for food and drinks Can put own shoes on (but not tie any laces) Can feed self with a spoon and make only a little mess
Always active and into everything Emotionally very dependent on adults Does not like to share anything	Can use a spoon and fork to eat with Goes to the toilet instead of wetting nappies in the daytime
Beginning to share things Shows affection toward younger children Less likely to have temper tantrums	Doesn't wet the bed overnight

Figure 7   *Childhood is the life stage between 1 year and 11 years old*

Childhood

Following infancy we come to childhood, which lasts from about one year to ten or eleven years.

The two main parts of childhood are the pre-school years (from one up to four or five years old), and the primary school years.

The pre-school child is aged from one to five years; the primary school years start at four to five, and finish at eleven.

PIES

If you have already completed Element 1.2 you will know something about this, but doing it again will help you to remember it.

When people develop, it is in more than one way. Some of the ways we develop are

- Physically – our bodies grow and change
- Intellectually – our minds develop
- Emotionally – we learn more about our feelings
- Socially – we learn how to live with other people.

The initials of these words spell out **PIES**, which makes it easier to remember them.

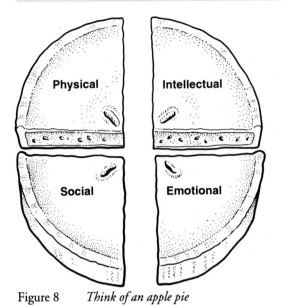

Figure 8   *Think of an apple pie*

Think of apple pies or mince pies (see Figure 8).

Student activity I

- Why not organise a photograph quiz for everybody in the class, and include your teachers?
- Get as many people as you can to bring in a photograph of themselves when they were a child, making sure that they put their names on the back.
- One person has to do the job of looking after the photographs and a list of who they are. Put the pictures on to a large piece of card, or on to a notice board.
- Give each picture a letter or a number, and keep a list of who they are where nobody else can see it. For example
  A – John
  B – Karen
  C – Sushita
  D – Mrs Jones, and so on (see Figure 9, page 20).
  Don't let anybody cheat by looking at the backs of the photographs. They should write

down who they think each photo is of and at what stage of development they think they were (baby, toddler, infant, etc.).

Adolescence

Puberty is when the body of a child starts to change into the body of an adult. Things are changing on the inside where we cannot see and on the outside where we can see.

Remember to include some of the changes that happened to you in the story about yourself growing up (see Student activity 2). Girls and boys end up looking very different at the end of puberty to how they looked before, and very different from each other.

Self-check questions

1 As the primary years end at 11, does that mean that adolescence starts when you are 11 and go to the secondary school? What do you think?
2 Were you an adolescent at 11?
3 What does puberty have to do with adolescence?

Adulthood

Adulthood starts when we are 18 years old as far as the law is concerned. That is the age when you can vote, and so are considered an adult for most things. Adulthood can be split into different stages as well, as it lasts for such a big proportion of our lives.

YOUNG ADULTS

As time passes by, we stop being adolescents. Adolescents are often also called teenagers, so

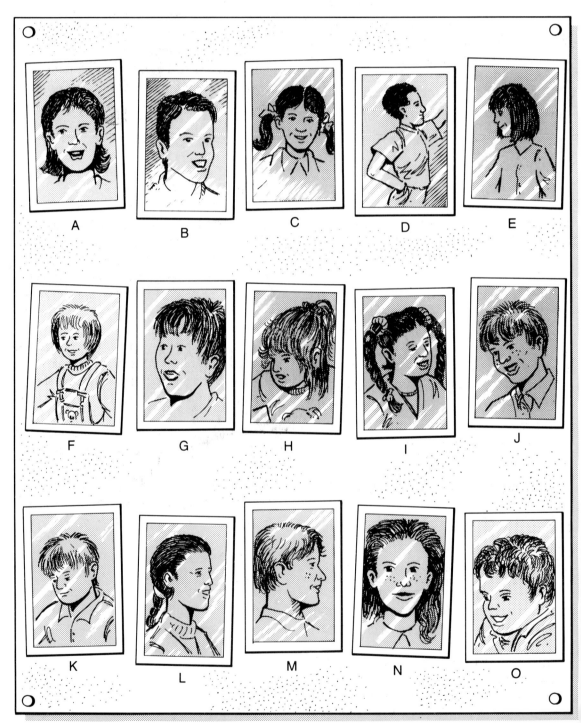

Figure 9   *Organise a photo quiz*

does that mean that on our eighteenth birthday we are grown up?

It does not really. We said before that the ages when we change from one stage of development to another are not exact. But it is some time around our late teens or early 20s that we move on to become a young adult. We are often said to be young adults until we are about 40, or even 45.

Middle age

From 40 or 45, we become middle aged. This lasts until we are around 65 (some people say 60, because some women can still retire at 60).

Elders

After 65 we become old-aged, or elderly. This stage of life is getting longer as people stay more healthy and active. Some experts now divide elders into 'active elders' from 65 to 70 or 75, and 'elders' from then on.

It is still true that there are more female elders than there are male elders, as women tend to live longer than men.

Student activity 2

DEVELOPMENT ACTIVITY

Read what is written about each of the people below, and then decide what stage in their lives each of them are at.

- John takes the dog for a walk each morning before breakfast. When he gets back home he has something to eat and then sits and reads his paper and listens to the radio until lunch time. After having some food, he goes to sleep in his favourite chair. Then he takes the dog for another walk, comes home for his dinner, and watches television until about 9.30 pm or 10 pm, when he goes to bed. Once a week he goes to the post office for his pension.

- Julie gets up in time to get the children ready for school and get their breakfast and packed lunch ready. After taking the children to school, she does the washing up and the cleaning and the laundry. Sometimes she goes to the shops on the way back from the school; sometimes she goes in the afternoon when she goes to collect the children again.

- Rafa wakes up every four or five hours and screams until he is fed. When he is not lying down, he is usually in his mother's arms.

- Kylie wakes up early in the morning and climbs over the side of her cot. She plays on the floor with her toys and anything else she can find, gurgling and talking to herself. She moves around in any way she can, and gets into all the cupboards and any bags or boxes she can find. The place is always a mess when Kylie is awake.

- Florrie has help to get up in the mornings. She spends most of her day sitting in a chair reading. She likes the large print books she can get from the visiting library. She does not eat much, just snack meals a few times a day. In the evening she has help to get to bed, and watches television for about an hour before she falls asleep.

- Wayne gets up in the afternoon, watches television then goes out and gets something to eat at McDonalds. He goes round the pubs and clubs with his mates, and gets home to bed at about 3am.

See Appendix for answers.

Figure 10   *People deal with old age differently*

SOCIAL FACTORS INFLUENCING PERSONAL DEVELOPMENT

As you will have noticed by now, not everybody is the same. Some of the differences are physical – we may be fat or thin, some of us are short and some tall.

There are also other differences which are more to do with the way we live and the place we live (the environment). Other factors which can make us change are events that happen to us. It may be the people we meet or the things that we do.

If you have a relative who is in the police force, and you like them a lot, you may decide you want to join the police force yourself.

The family

A very big influence on the way you grow up is the family that you live with. If your parents are farmers, you grow up with animals, plants and trees around you all the time. When it is time to look for a job, you may want to do the same as them. You may have had enough of that and want to move to live in a city. In either case, living with your family has had an influence on you.

Figure 11   *The environment you grow up in influences your life*

Not all families are like the one that you live in. There are many different types of group which are still called a family. The first group most people think of is where there is a mother, a father and their children.

Lots of families today will have only one parent. These are called 'one-parent families', and that parent is often (but not always) the mother. There are also fathers who bring up children alone.

Sometimes children live with their grandparents, or just one grandparent. Many people get married more than once, and the person your parent marries would then be your step-parent. So there are stepmothers and stepfathers; if they have children of their own, they are stepchildren to the new parent.

Both sets of children will then have stepbrothers and/or stepsisters.

Children cannot always live with members of their family, and other families will take them in as foster children or as adopted children.

The kind of family we live with during our childhood can have an influence on the way we behave and the way we are when we are adolescents and adults.

Self-check question

✔ 1 Do you know the difference between being fostered and being adopted? If not, find out, and write a paragraph about each.

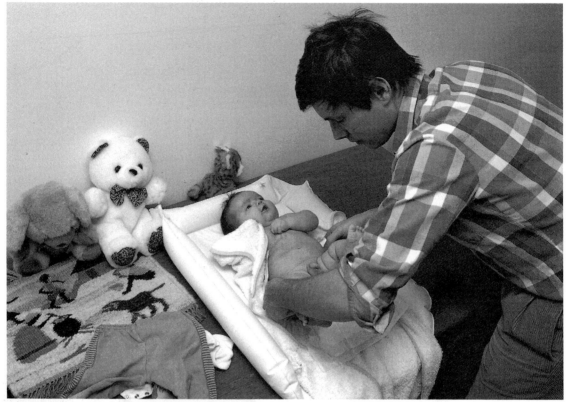

Figure 12   *A one-parent family might be father and son*

Student activity 3

Read about these children, and answer the questions about how their family life may have influenced them.

- Chris is an only child aged three. Both parents work in very good jobs, and Chris is looked after by a nanny during the day. There are not many chances to meet other children. Because of this

  A Chris may not know how to share things with other children
  B Chris may be very clever
  C Chris may sleep a lot.

- Joydip and Sanjay are aged seven years and nine years and live with their grandmother. Their parents work abroad, and can only come and visit a few times a year. Gran is quite old and cannot walk very far. She is also getting deaf. Because of this

  A Joydip and Sanjay may not like each other
  B Joydip and Sanjay may be very close to each other
  C Joydip and Sanjay may speak very quietly.

- Mr and Mrs Smith have both been married twice. They have seven children between them, and live in a ground floor flat with four bedrooms. The children are aged between two years and fourteen years. Because of this

  A The children may not get enough to eat
  B The children may all be very shy
  C The children may have no problem mixing with other people.

- Lesley lived with her mother until her mother died of a drug overdose when Lesley was nine years old. She then went to live with her gran, but gran got very ill and couldn't look after her any more. An aunt and her boyfriend took her in, but that didn't work out, and she had to go into care. At first she was in a children's home, but after a few weeks she went to some foster parents. That lasted a few months and then she went to some different foster parents. They wanted to adopt her, but she did not like them so she ran away. She had to go back to a children's home then. Because of this

A Lesley does not trust adults any more
B Lesley wants to go to another foster home
C Lesley is a very happy girl.

See Appendix for answers.

Education

Formal education starts when we go to school. In this country that is when we are four or five years old. The age is not the same for everybody. It depends where you live and when your birthday is. Some nursery schools start to teach children before they are this age, and if a child has special needs because they are disabled in some way, they can start their education as early as two years old.

Going to a nursery or playgroup is often the first time away from home with people who are not members of the family. But for others, going to school is the first time away from a parent. That is why you sometimes see little children crying and screaming and

Figure 13   *School paygroup may be the first time away from the family*

clinging to their parent at the school gates. They are frightened to leave the parent in case they do not come back. They are not used to being left alone.

Children can go to private schools as well as state schools. If they go to a private school, somebody has to pay the bills. This is usually the parent or some other relative, but sometimes it is tied up with the parent's job. When a parent is in the army, for instance, they may have to go places where it is not safe for children. The army will pay for a school, then. Some of these schools are 'residential', which means that you have to live there as well as attend lessons there. Parents also send children there because they think that they will be given a better education.

Some of the things that children do when they first go to school look like just playing. Things like playing houses, playing cooking, playing doctors and nurses. These games help them learn.

Children also like to do 'messy' things, like painting or playing with water and sand.

- How do you think that doing things like this can help children to learn?

When we get into the other classes, the lessons are more serious, and we have to listen to the teacher. When we get older still, we have to do more of the learning ourselves. That is what you are expected to do in this course – do more of the learning for yourself.

Most people attend school until they are 16 years old. Quite a lot of teenagers do not like school, and stay away. This is called 'truancy'. Others behave so badly when they are there, that the school asks them to stay away. If they have to stay away for a short time, it is called 'suspension'. If they are never to be allowed back, this is known as 'exclusion', or being expelled.

- What effect do you think there will be on pupils who are suspended or expelled?

After 16, you can carry on being educated at colleges. After you are 18, you can go to colleges or universities. You can also do educational courses at night school or by post. Really, when you think about it, there is no end to education if you do not want it to end.

One reason people stop going to school, or want to carry on learning after they finish school is the influence of the teachers. Many people decide to be teachers themselves because they like their own teacher so much!

Self-check questions

1 At what age do children start school?
2 At what age can children with special needs start their education?
3 Why do some children cry and cling to their mothers at the school gate?
4 What is the difference between residential schools and ordinary day schools?
5 At what age can children leave school?
6 What is truancy?
7 What does being expelled from school mean?
8 What do you think of the teachers you have had so far in your life?
9 Which one or which ones have had the most influence on you?
10 Was it a good influence or a bad influence?

See Appendix for answers.

Environment

Our environment is the place where we live, the places we go, and the things we use, such as the parks and the leisure centres. One of the main parts of your environment which will affect your personal development is the place in which you live. The kind of places that most people live in are houses and flats, and they both come in many different shapes and sizes.

They are also different ages, and kept in different states of repair. A house with a leaking roof, or mould growing on the walls because of the damp is certainly going to affect the people living there. It is generally better for people to have space around them, so small terraced houses with two bedrooms are fine for two or three people to live in. If parents with four children lived there, it would be very crowded, and affect the children's development.

People also live in mobile homes, which actually stay in one place and are like big caravans. These are usually out in the countryside, not in towns. Others really do move around a lot, such as gypsies and new age travellers, who live in smaller caravans, converted buses, vans, and even cars.

Student activity 4

 • How do you think children living in a damp flat which is seven floors up in a big block of flats will be affected?

• What would be the effect on the seven children living in a two-bedroomed terraced house?

• What sort of life would the children in a travelling family lead? How would their development be affected?

• If you had a free choice, what sort of home would you like to have?

GREEN SPACES

Green spaces are an important part of our environment. Some of us have much more than others; those living in the countryside are surrounded by green space. Those living in towns might have a garden, but they may have to go and find a park or a playing field before they see any green spaces. There may be woods, commons, or forests near you. These are all good places to go for walks or picnics away from the concrete and bricks you see every day.

LEISURE FACILITIES

These are the places you go to when you want to go out and enjoy yourself, or do something different. The leisure facility may be the green space we have just been talking about. It may also be your local leisure centre.

Self-check questions

 1 Where are the green spaces that you can easily get to?

2 How often do you use them?

3 What sort of other people are there when you go?

4 Are there any sports that you do, either in the college or away from it?

5 Or do you go to nightclubs and the disco and get your exercise there?

6 Make a list of the leisure facilities in your area, and write a note about what you think of the ones you use yourself.

Student activity 5

Think of all these things together – housing, green spaces and leisure facilities. Where do you think would be the best place for these people to live?

- Shane and Vicky, who are 21 and 22, and have just got married.
- Mrs Sturton, who is retired and widowed.
- John and Sandra, and their children who are six years and eight years old.
- Mr and Mrs Curley, whose three children have now all left home. They live in the town, but want to move away.

Peer groups

Getting out and about also gives you a chance to meet other people. If you play tennis, you will meet other people who like to play tennis. If you play football, you meet other players. It is the same if you go dancing; you meet other dancers. These other people who are interested in the same thing as you are can be called your 'peer group'. When you are in college, the other people on this foundation course with you are your peer group. We belong to different peer groups for different things, so we might belong to quite a lot of peer groups.

Peer groups are another way we are influenced in our development. If we want to stay friends with the other people in our peer groups, we will often change the way we behave so that it fits in. This may be staying out later than our parents want us to, or smoking, or taking drugs, because all the others do. Or it may be going to the youth club on Thursday nights so that you can meet the others and play games or sport together. The influences of peer groups can be bad or good, such as staying away from school, or all going to get a Duke of Edinburgh's Award for Community Service. We will be members of peer groups at all stages in our lives, people we work with, go to the pub with, or live near.

Self-check questions

1 Do you hang around with a gang of people about your own age? They might live near you, but some may live further away. This is another example of a peer group.
2 Make a list of all the peer groups you think you may be a member of.

Economic factors

We know about some of the social factors which can affect our lives now. There are other factors which affect us too, such as economic factors.

Economic factors involve how much money you and your family get and how much is spent. Both of these can have an effect on your personal development. One of these effects was mentioned previously – if your parents have the money and want to send you away to school, then they can do. If your parents would like to send you away to school, but do not have the money to pay for it, then you probably will not go.

'Income' is the word used to describe the money we have coming in. It may be from wages, or it may be from benefits such as Jobseekers' Allowance. Some people have an income that is not from either of these. They may own property, such as houses, flats, shops or offices, and have an income from letting them to other people. Sometimes, people have a lot of money from investing in shares, or winning the pools or the lottery. This money is made to 'work' for them (invested), and gives them a regular income.

Student activity 6

- Collect copies of your local paper, and some caring magazines such as *Nursing Standard*, *Care Weekly* and *Community Care*. Look at all the different job advertisements, and see how much people doing different caring jobs can earn.
- What difference will it make if the person doing that job lives alone, or has to support a partner and family with the same amount of money?

FINANCIAL COMMITMENTS

Wherever our money comes from, it will soon be spent. Some of it will go on 'financial commitments', which are the things you cannot really avoid paying for. This includes (for most of us) somewhere to live, so we have to pay rent or a mortgage. There will also be the regular bills to pay, such as electricity, gas, water, television licence, and Council Tax.

If we have children, we have a commitment to them. We have to keep them clothed and fed, as well as ourselves. If we run a car, that becomes a commitment – even if it is one we can get rid of, if we really want to.

Other commitments might be paying off loans we have had to buy things, or a student loan that we used to live on when we were at college.

Self-check questions

1 Think about what commitments you have, and which your parents have. Which ones could you manage without, and which ones you could not manage without?
2 There are other ways to spend money, which are not really commitments. How much do you spend going to a nightclub, or the cinema, bowling, skating, or going for a drink?

Student activity 7

CASE HISTORIES

Look at these case histories and say what commitments each of the three people have. If your teacher wants to add some figures here, you could have some numeracy work for your portfolio.

- Lewis rents a bedsit. He is a student. The television comes with the room, but he is buying a music centre on hire purchase. There is no washing machine, so he has to go to a launderette.
- Janice is a single parent with two children, aged three and seven. She lives in a council house. There is a television, and a second-hand music centre. Her income is from state benefits, and she borrows from a moneylender to buy Christmas and birthday presents for her children.
- Adrian and Maureen are living together in a house they are buying on a new estate. They both have good jobs, and have borrowed money from the bank to put everything they want into the house. All the furniture and electrical goods such as television, video, remote control CD player, washing machine, spindryer and dishwasher were bought with a bank loan.

Figure 14   *Economic circumstances can change – you may even win the lottery!*

Student activity 8

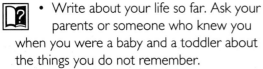 • Write about your life so far. Ask your parents or someone who knew you when you were a baby and a toddler about the things you do not remember.
• If you can find any photographs to go with your story, you can see how different you, your family and friends looked at different ages.
• Think about how you have been affected by social and economic factors, and write about that as well.

• Use the headings from PIES to help you write your story.
• How do you think your personal development could be affected if
  A your economic circumstances were different? e.g. you had less money or more money than you do now
  B the environment you live in was different (you lived in a different place)?
• What changes would you like to make to your social and economic circumstances?

If you do not want to write about yourself, you could write about someone else, or make up a story about a person of your age.

This work will give you your portfolio evidence for Unit 2, Element 1, Performance Criteria 5 of Foundation GNVQ.

Explore relationships at different life stages

At the end of this section you will be able to

- identify relationships formed at different life stages
- describe the main characteristics of relationships formed at different life stages
- describe the effects of forming positive and negative personal relationships at each life stage
- suggest the effects of positive and negative relationships on personal development.

RELATIONSHIPS

We all have relationships with other people in our lives. The first relationships are normally with other members of our family – mother, father and any brothers and sisters. There are also possible links with the members of our 'extended family', such as grandparents, aunts, uncles and cousins. We make another set of relationships when we start to do things outside the home.

Self-check questions

1 When we are very small, where is the first place we are likely to go away from our homes and families and have time to meet and make relationships with other people?
   A playgroup
   B school
   C work.
2 Where do we make most of our relationships when we are aged between five years and sixteen years?
   A church
   B family
   C school.

3 When are people most likely to have a serious relationship which could end in marriage?
   A 14 to 16 years old
   B 18 to 25 years old
   C 50 to 65 years old.
4 If you are said to 'have a good relationship' with someone it means
   A You are married to them
   B You get on very well with them
   C They are related to you.
5 The age when people are most likely to have friends of the same sex is
   A 5 to 10 years old
   B 15 to 20 years old
   C 30 to 40 years old.

See Appendix for answers.

The relationships people have at different ages are of different kinds. The first relationships we have are dependency relationships. This is because a child is dependent on the parents for all its needs. When people become adults, there are still some dependency relationships, where one person relies on the other for meeting all their needs.

Sometimes it is when a person is ill or disabled and needs caring for. So a nurse or a carer are in a dependency relationship with their patients and clients.

Figure 15   *Our extended family*

Student activity 9

- Arrange to watch children playing at a playgroup or in a nursery or nursery class. Have a look at how much they play together, or if they play by themselves.
- What do you think?

The children may be playing near each other, but when they are between about two and three years old, they are not really playing together. They may fight because they want the same toy, but that is not really playing together. The only relationship between them is that they are near each other.

After about the age of three, there is some evidence of relationships forming. They will play at cooking, or house, and one will be daddy while the other is mummy. They are *sharing* the game.

This is the start of friendship. When we start to go out of our homes and meet other people, we can begin to choose who to have

relationships with. When starting school, there is a class full of other children. Some may know each other because they live near each other, and went to the same playgroup or childminder. A lot will be new faces, and that gives some choice in who to be friends with. We will have relationships with the others, and with teachers and other staff at school, such as the lunchtime supervisors and the caretaker, but that does not mean we will be friends. A relationship does not have to be a friendship. The same sort of thing happens when you move up from one school to the next school.

If you go to college, you will meet another set of new faces. You will have relationships and decide who to make friends with again.

When you are sharing the same experiences, you can *support* each other. This is one of the benefits of relationships.

As we get older, we start to notice the *physical attractions* of other people – the shape of their bodies, whether they have a

Figure 16   *From the age of three upwards, children begin to form relationships or friendships with other children*

nice smile, or if their hair is attractive. When we have noticed any of these physical attractions, we start to look for a chance to start a relationship with them. This is how many romances start, and the relationship becomes *sexual.*

Another kind of relationship is the *power* relationship. The teacher in a class full of children is the person with the power. The carer in a retirement home is the one with the power. At home, parents are the ones with the power. If you remember what we said above about dependency relationships, you can see that power and dependency are very close to each other.

When we go to work, the people in charge are in a power relationship with us. The people we are working with have another kind – this is called a *working relationship.* You may not be friends with many of the people at work, but you can still get on well together when you are doing the job. If you like each other enough, you will start to see each other away from work, and become friends. The relationship will then become more sharing and supporting, possibly even becoming sexual.

Self-check questions

 I Who do most of us have our first relationship with?

A friends
B parents
C teachers

Figure 17   *Romantic relationships often start with physical attraction*

2 When do we make our second set of
   relationships?
   A when we start to go outside our homes
   B when we start to walk
   C when we start school
3 What sort of relationship is the one between
   parents and young children?
   A sexual
   B dependency
   C sharing
4 Which is a dependency relationship?
   A boyfriend and girlfriend
   B schoolfriends
   C nurse and patient
5 What is one of the benefits of having friends?
   A support
   B power
   C dependency
6 What kind of relationship might a physical
   attraction lead to?

   A power
   B sexual
   C working
7 Read this short piece about relationships with
   parents, and then explain it in your own
   words. You may also want to have a class
   discussion about it, but write down what
   you personally think it means before you do
   that.

   'When I was five, my parents knew
   everything. When I was fifteen, my parents
   knew nothing. When I was twenty-five, I was
   surprised by how much my parents had
   learned in the past ten years!'

Figure 18   *A power relationship*

The effects of relationships

Relationships can have both good effects and bad effects; or no effects at all. Read through the following situations, and then say whether you think the effects of the relationship described has been good, bad, or had no effect. Give reasons for why you decided as you did.

- Diane is 14, and her parents have just started to allow her to go out on Friday and Saturday evenings. They take her and collect her, and sometimes her friends. In the disco, she meets some other girls who are a bit older than her. They offer her cigarettes. She tells them she does not smoke, but they call her a baby and sneer at her for being soft. She really wants to be friends with them, so when she goes the next week, she starts to smoke cigarettes.

- Darren is 15. He has just moved to a new flat with his parents. He does not know anyone around, but does not want to stay in. He goes out and just messes about because he is bored. He throws rubbish at cats and dogs, scratches cars, and throws stones at windows in empty buildings.

    He is kicking a can at a dog one evening when John and Mark come out of a house nearby and tell him to stop it. He gets talking to them, and they offer to take him to the snooker club they are going to. Darren did not know there was a snooker club, and had never played, but he had seen the game on television.

That was a few months ago, and Darren is now a very good snooker player, and goes to the club whenever he can, and socialises with people he has met there at other times.

- Dahlia is 25 and went on an outward bound weekend with her colleagues from work. There were other people at the same centre when she was there. They were all staying for a week. She met Mark there. They became friendly, and did as much together during the week as they could. They kissed a couple of times. At the end of the week, they gave each other their addresses and phone numbers. That was a year ago, and they have not made any contact with each other since then.

- Steve is 13 and not doing very well at school. He has started to miss a day every week. The headmistress has found out, and called him in for an interview. Steve tells her that one of the teachers is always picking on him, and that was the day he did not come to school.

- Walter is a widower living by himself. He felt very lonely, so he started dance classes on two afternoons a week. This took him out of the house and helped him to meet new people, especially ladies. He started talking to Ellen, who only lived a few doors away from him. They soon started calling on each other for a cup of tea and a chat on the days they did not go dancing.

Student activity 10

- Using all the information you have learned from doing this unit, write a short piece about what you think the main types of relationship are at each life stage. Remember that the stages are infants, children, adolescents, adults and elders.
- Using the same style as the case histories above, make some up to show what you mean for different age groups.
- If you can think of any relationships of your own which you do not mind sharing, write about those, and say whether they were good or bad for you or the other person.

This will all provide portfolio evidence for Element 2.2.

Explore relationships between clients and carers

At the end of this section, you should be able to

- describe what contributes to forming effective relationships between clients and carers
- identify different needs of clients
- explain ways in which clients' needs are met by carers
- describe barriers to forming effective relationships between client and carer.

CLIENTS

'Clients' is one of the names given to the people who need looking after. They are called 'patients' in hospitals and nursing homes. In many social care settings they are known as 'users' or 'service users'. Some private agencies may call them 'customers'.

The main client groups are children, elders, and people with special needs – these include people with physical disabilities, people with learning difficulties, and people with mental health problems.

People may also need caring for because they are ill or injured; this is when they are more likely to be called patients. Other groups who may need care, but fit into none of the other groups, are pregnant women and those who have just had babies.

CARERS

Most carers are from the same family as the person being cared for. You will remember that one of the main client groups is children. They are looked after by their parents more than anybody else. Children are also looked after by grandparents, brothers, sisters, aunts and uncles.

They may just be helping out by baby-sitting now and again, or the children sometimes live with them all the time.

Another of the main client groups is elders. They are also looked after by members of their family more of the time than anybody else. Often it is a partner, but it can also be one of their children. Sometimes it is the grandchild or niece and nephew, or sometimes a brother or sister who does the caring.

Friends and neighbours may help in lots of different ways, as well. It may be by doing the shopping, or making extra food so that they can take a meal round. Or it may be by staying for an hour or two, or even all night if that is what is needed.

All of these people, family, friends and neighbours, are called 'informal carers'. They do not belong to any organisations or get paid any wages.

'Professional carers' are the carers who get paid to do the job. They are the nurses, doctors, home care workers, residential workers, care assistants and so on, who are paid wages to look after other people. You will learn more about this from Chapter 3 of this foundation course.

'Voluntary carers' make up the third group of people who look after others. Volunteers are not related to the clients or patients, and are not paid any wages for the help they give. They might have their expenses paid, such as bus fares or petrol money. Usually they belong to a voluntary organisation. Some voluntary organisations which may be near you are

- Hospital League of Friends (who take patients home or drive them for clinics at out-patients, as well as other occasions)
- Crossroads, who have volunteers to go and look after clients or patients while their family carers have some time off
- Community Service Volunteers (CSV), who do many things all over the country involving work with children, elders, and people with special needs. They are at 732 Pentonville Road, London N1 9NJ, telephone 0171 278 6601.

There are also many local voluntary organisations which you can find out about from your local library.

Figure 19   *Some people need help to attend clinics*

Needs of clients

What clients need starts from the same base as everybody else. This is food, water, warmth and respect. The difference is that they may need more help to have these needs met than other people.

Apart from these needs that everybody has, each person has needs of their own. A person with one leg will need a different kind of help to a person with one arm, a blind person needs a different kind of help to a deaf person.

 A good way to remember what people need is to think of **SPICE**

- Social needs
- Physical needs
- Intellectual needs
- Cultural needs
- Emotional needs.

Student activity 11

 Here is a list of things which carers do for clients. Decide which task is meeting which need from SPICE.

1   help to go to the toilet
2   reading from a story book
3   making sandwiches
4   taking to church/mosque/synagogue
5   organising a bingo session
6   listening to personal problems
7   help to get over a bereavement
8   taking to the cinema.

See Appendix for answers.

Ways of meeting needs

The physical needs of clients are met by carers doing the things for them which they are unable to do for themselves. These will include feeding, dressing, washing, bathing, helping to the toilet, brushing teeth and keeping the mouth clean.

There are also other needs to meet by communicating effectively, providing information, encouraging choice, and recognising the client as an individual with their own personal and cultural differences.

Relationships between clients and carers

Relationships between people can be either good or bad. As a carer, it is up to you to try to make any relationship a good one. Clients may have many other problems to worry about, and so may seem rude or selfish sometimes.

There are some things you should think about when you look after other people. One of them is mentioned above – the client has other problems on their mind apart from their relationship with their carer.

Keeping a client happy is a very important part of a carer's job. One way to do this is to always remember that you are dealing with a person like yourself. Even if the client is very young, or they have a disability which stops them from talking to you, they are individuals who should be treated with respect. This is known as 'recognising their individual identity'.

Treating with respect also means allowing as much privacy as possible. Knock on bedroom doors before walking in, close toilet doors when you have helped your client to

get in there, do not listen to telephone conversations when you help someone make a call.

Giving choice whenever you can is also a good way to show a client that you recognise they are an individual. If you need to help get a client dressed, allow them to choose their clothes as best they can. If someone cannot talk, they may be able to nod or shake their head or point to things held up for them to see.

Being in a rush because you have six people to get ready is not an excuse to refuse choice. Showing a real interest in your clients, and finding out about them can improve relationships a great deal.

Student activity 12

 • Make a list of the things you think you should know about clients you are looking after.

Do not read on until after you have made your list.

Things you need to know

Some of the things you may need to know are

- Name. What do they like to be called? John Smith may like to be called 'Johnny', or he may prefer 'John', or 'Mr Smith'.
- Diet. Not just special diets (such as diabetic diet, or salt-free diet), but personal likes and dislikes. Do they prefer tea or coffee, white or brown bread?
- Religion. Are they religious? If so, do they have any special needs, such as what they should wear and the food they may and may not eat? Also are there any special

days or festivals they may need help in celebrating?

- Family and friends. Are there any relatives or friends? Do they know where the client is at the moment? Is any help needed to keep in touch – making 'phone calls or helping to make 'phone calls? Help with reading or writing letters? If the client is in residential care, is there anybody they prefer to sit with – or to sit well away from?
- Cleanliness. Do they prefer a bath or a shower? Which toothpaste do they like? Which soap and shampoo?
- Entertainment. Which television shows do they like to watch? Do they like bingo? Which magazines or newspapers do they read? Which radio station or which type of music on tape or CD would they like to listen to?
- What care they need. Do they need help with washing, dressing, brushing hair, or going to the toilet? Can they feed themselves? How much help do they need to get out of and back into bed? Do they need their mouth or nose wiped regularly? Do they need their position in the armchair changed now and again? Do they like an afternoon nap?
- What is the best way to communicate? Talking is the way we usually do this, as well as the body language that goes with the words. Some people cannot understand or hear spoken language, but can see the body language. Smile and be gentle in your movements, friendliness can be communicated without words.

If you know all these things and more about your client, and you use what you know to meet their needs, your chances of having a good relationship with them are very much improved.

Confidentiality

One result of developing a good relationship is that clients will begin to trust you. If people trust you, they may start to tell you things in confidence. This means that they could be telling you secrets. If you are told secrets, you should keep them to yourself. If any of the secrets worry you, such as 'I am going to take an overdose of my pills tonight', then you should tell the client that you have to see your manager about it.

If it is a secret about the past, e.g. 'I took an overdose five years ago', or 'I was in prison 25 years ago', then it should be kept between you and the client. If they wish to tell anybody else, it is up to them, not you – unless the client asks you to tell somebody else.

Telling tales you are not supposed to can get you into a lot of trouble when you are a professional carer. Even if you go out on work placements, you should not talk about the people you are helping to look after. If you do any writing about clients for college, give them a false name.

Providing information

Providing information is another important task that carers do. Simple things, such as what time dinner will be ready, or when the doctor will be visiting can be very useful to a client who depends on you.

There are also more complicated things which clients may want to know: how to complain, when and how to take their medicine, etc. If you do not know, you should find out for them, or find somebody who can help them.

Figure 20   *A good relationship is important*

BARRIERS TO FORMING EFFECTIVE RELATIONSHIPS

Sometimes it is difficult to get along with people, no matter how much you try. At other times there are reasons which can be put right if you stop to think about why there is a problem.

The main reason that there are sometimes barriers to forming good relationships with clients is because carers do not take any notice of the kind of advice given above. If clients are treated as just another one of the crowd, then there is no respect being shown. If carers are always too busy to stop and talk to clients, and lose their tempers because of the stress, they will not be doing a very good job. They may be keeping the place clean and tidy, but it is just as important to keep people happy.

A useful saying is, 'It isn't what you say, it's the way that you say it'. If you say something in a temper (aggressively), you upset people. If you say the same thing using different words, and with a smile, people are more likely to be on your side.

Student activity 13

- Practise saying 'I haven't got time, you'll have to wait' in a grumpy voice. Then say 'I'll be with you in a minute, I've just got to take this to Mrs Smith'. Or 'You've got to have a bath now', and 'The bath is ready for you now, lovely and warm'.

  Try some other grumpy ways to say things which you might have to say when you are a carer, and then find a nicer way to say them. Ask your teacher for help if you cannot think of any.

Self-check questions

1 Give two other names for a 'client'.
2 What are clients called in hospitals?
3 Name two client groups.
4 What is a professional carer?
5 Who does most of the caring?
  A the doctor
  B nurses
  C family
  D friends
6 What is a good way to remember people's needs?
  A RICE
  B SPICE
  C HERBS
  D GRASS
7 Confidentiality means
  A keeping secrets
  B being confident
  C working quietly
  D knowing the answers.
8 Write down three things you should know about clients.
9 A barrier to good relationships with clients is
  A having time to spare
  B respecting confidentiality
  C communicating well
  D aggressiveness.
10 Explain the saying 'It's not what you say, but the way that you say it'.

See Appendix for answers.

3

INVESTIGATING WORKING IN HEALTH AND SOCIAL CARE

ELEMENT 3.1

Working in UK health and social care services

At the end of this section, you will have

- identified the main providers of health and social care, and given examples of the main types of service they provide
- identified and given the main purpose of the job roles in health and medical care

- identified and given the main purpose of the job roles in health and medical care
- identified and given the main purposes of the job roles in community care and support
- identified and given the main purpose of the job roles in indirect care.

HEALTH CARE AND SOCIAL CARE

In order to make a decision about working in the health and social care services, first we need to look at what health care and social care actually are. Until the 1990 National Health Service and Community Care Act was introduced, health care and social care were usually seen as quite separate things.

Student activity 1

- Write down a sentence to say what you think 'caring' is.
- Write down a few words to tell your teacher what you think health care is.
- Then write down a few words to tell your teacher what you think social care is.

- Write down what you think the difference is between them.
- Why are you on a caring course? Write a few sentences to say why you chose to do a caring course.

- Now read the following definition: Caring means looking after other people, and any job which involves looking after other people is now known as a caring job, or part of the caring profession. The people who do the caring are called carers.

WELFARE STATE

The modern welfare state began after the second world war as the result of a report by politician William Beveridge. His idea was to take money out of the wages of people who were working and use it to pay for a national health service to care for anybody who was ill, and they would not have to pay for it. He also started a national insurance scheme which allowed people to claim money when they were unemployed or sick. Both of these schemes were agreed by the Government, and started in 1946. Some changes have been made since then, but the main idea of not allowing anyone to starve to death, and letting everyone have treatment when they are ill, is still there.

Health care

This is looking after people who are ill in some way. It is not only physical illness, but also mental illness.

Hospitals are the biggest places which provide health care services, but health care is taking place in people's own homes more and more. This is known as 'community care'. The number of people who need to go into hospital is less than it used to be, and those who do need to go in do not stay as long as they once might have done.

There are other places which provide health care, such as nursing homes, hospices (which are like small hospitals, but only for people who are terminally ill), hostels for people getting over a mental illness, and day centres. Health centres run by family doctors also give treatments now which you could only get in hospitals before, such as removing warts or ingrowing toe nails. Other types of health care which you can get in the community are from dentists and opticians, chiropodists and chemists (pharmacists).

Maternity services (for pregnant women) are available both in hospitals and in the mother's own home. Private nursing homes can also provide a maternity service. Family doctors, midwives and health visitors provide a 'domiciliary service' – this means looking after people at home, by visiting each person separately.

Social care

Social care refers to the help given by social services departments (SSDs) to people with 'social problems', such as child abuse, learning difficulties (which used to be called mental handicap), money problems or family violence. The SSDs also provide a service to children and young people who have been in trouble with the police.

In Scotland this is done by the social work departments (SWDs). Disabled people and people with learning difficulties are not always ill in any way, but they may need some help with day-to-day living.

People who have been ill may need help when the illness is over. After a stroke, for instance, help may be needed with getting dressed or cooking food. When having a baby, some women may need help with looking after their other children, or the housework. This kind of help is social care.

Self-check questions

1 What are the biggest places where you can get health care?

2 Name two other places where health care is given.

3 What does 'domiciliary' mean? (You can use a dictionary to look this up if you need to.)

4 What do the initials SSD stand for? If you are in Scotland, what do the initials SWD stand for?

5 Name four services that the SSDs and SWDs provide.

Figure 21   *Home helps provide a service*

6 What sort of help may a person need after a stroke?
7 What sort of help may some women need after having a baby?
8 Name four services provided by the National Health Service.

Student activity 2

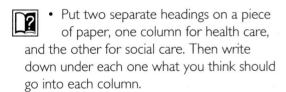

• Put two separate headings on a piece of paper, one column for health care, and the other for social care. Then write down under each one what you think should go into each column.

If you would like some clues about what sort of things we are talking about, use the following list and put the services mentioned into the correct column.

• Accident and emergency department
• Day nursery
• Dentist
• Retirement homes

• Social workers
• Health visitors
• Home helps/home carers
• Doctors
• Opticians
• Playgroups
• Hospitals
• Nursing homes
• Social services department
• Children's homes
• Midwives

What do people do?

DOCTORS

Simon's training to become a doctor took seven years. After his training finished and he passed his exams, Simon had to gain experience in various kinds of medicine before picking the job he wanted to do. That meant specialising in one kind of work.

Most doctors work for the National Health Service, although there are some who work only with private patients. Some doctors work in specific settings, for example occupational health physicians work in industrial places such as factories, mines or offices. Others choose to work in the Army or the Navy.

Quite a lot want to be family doctors, also known as general practitioners (or GPs). They are said to be in general practice because they deal with everything that can go wrong with people. Patients either turn up at the surgery or call the doctor out when they are ill or injured. So family doctors deal with the general illnesses. General practitioners are different to the doctors who work in hospitals, who are 'specialists' in certain kinds of work. A GP will send (or 'refer') people to a specialist for advice or another opinion on something that he or she is not certain about, or for treatment that cannot be given at home, in the surgery or in a health centre.

A specialist is someone like a surgeon who will do an operation, or a cancer specialist who will arrange radiation treatment. They may also be psychiatrists, who deal with mental illness, or dermatologists who treat skin diseases. There are many specialisms, some you may have heard of and some you may not. A couple of the more common ones are paediatricians, specialising in the treatment of children, and geriatricians, dealing with the problems of old age.

Doctors can 'refer' people to social services departments if they think that their patients need social care, such as arranging changes in the houses of disabled people to allow them to manage better (ramps to replace steps to doors, lifts to get up the stairs, fitting a bathroom downstairs).

Social services also arrange for old people to go into retirement homes, if that is what they want to do.

More and more doctors are now working in health centres, sharing with other doctors and people from other caring professions (such as nurses, health visitors and midwives).

The first person you will meet is the receptionist, who will be responsible for taking your name and address, making an appointment for you, and then finding your medical records to give to the doctor when you arrive for the appointment.

Self-check questions

1 What do the initials GP stand for?
2 When a GP 'refers' a patient to a specialist, what does this mean?
3 Why are family doctors also called general practitioners?
4 What is the name given to a doctor who specialises in the treatment of children?
5 What sort of people does a geriatrician look after?
6 Name two caring professions working in health centres.
7 What does the receptionist at a health centre do?

Student activity 3

- Make some record cards like the one pictured in Figure 22. Fill it in for yourself, and use them in the next exercise. This will help toward achieving core skills (Communications 1.2).
- Make up a short play about going to see the doctor at a health centre. Somebody will have to pretend to be the doctor, and other people will play the receptionist and the patient. It is best to do this in small groups, not everyone has to act a part, but everyone

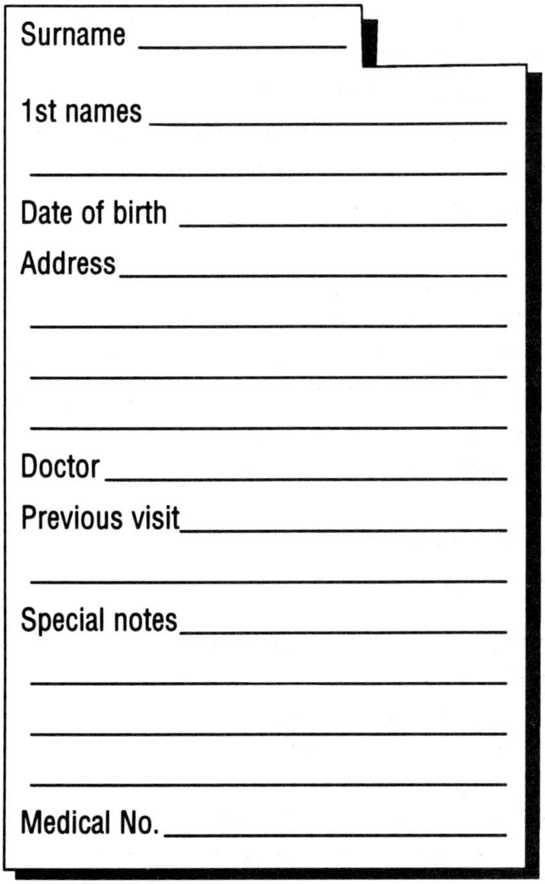

Surname _____
1st names _____
_____
Date of birth _____
Address _____
_____
_____
_____
Doctor _____
Previous visit _____
_____
Special notes _____
_____
_____
_____
Medical No. _____

Figure 22   *A simple record card*

should help with the planning. Each group should have a different role play to the other groups. You could start with the patient going to the receptionist and asking to see the doctor.

The receptionist will then say that the patient has to have an appointment, and ask questions about name, address, and what is wrong. The record card will then have to be found from the ones you filled in before. The patient could then argue that they want to see the doctor straight away, because it is urgent. Decide in your group if anyone is going to pretend to be angry, or follow the instructions they are told.

The next scene is with the patient seeing the doctor. Work out in your group what you think the doctor and the patient will say to each other.

- Afterwards, the other groups should say what they thought of the play. Is it what happens when you go to the doctor? For the 'actors', what was it like to be a doctor or receptionist or patient?

NURSES

Martin trained as a general nurse; his qualification is RGN, which stands for 'registered general nurse'. The course lasted three years. He went to a college, and on placements with qualified nurses in hospitals and in the community, and had to pass exams.

There are three other types of nurse training besides the RGN, all of them taking three years of study. One is working with mentally ill people – registered mental nurse (RMN). Another is the registered sick children's nurse (RSCN), and the last is the registered nurse for the mentally handicapped (RNMH).

When they are qualified, most nurses work in hospitals, but there are many other things they can do. Some of these other jobs mean that they have to do more training, for example if they want to be a midwife or a health visitor. Sometimes it is where they work and the kind of work they do which gives nurses a slightly different title. It is also possible to train as a midwife at some colleges of nursing without training to be a nurse first.

Practice nurses work in the surgery or health centre and do some of the work for the doctors, and also give some treatments which may otherwise have to be done in hospitals. The nurses will do things like taking blood pressure and testing urine, also giving advice on diets and how to look after sick people. Practice nurses also give treatments such as injections, putting on or changing dressings, and syringing ears (washing the wax out).

District nurses have similar responsibilities, but they visit people in their own homes and give people baths or help them to the toilet as well as give injections, change dressings, and so on. This is known as domiciliary visiting.

Health visitors (HVs) are nurses who have had extra training and visit people at home to educate them about health matters. They do most of their work with families who have children under 5 years old, but they are also involved with older people and people with disabilities.

Midwives may also work from doctors surgeries and health centres. Their job is to provide assistance and medical care to women during pregnancy, labour and childbirth and until the children are ten days old, when the health visitor takes over responsibility. Midwifery training and nursing are available to both men and women.

Most nurses work for local health authorities and trusts, but many work in private nursing homes, hospitals and residential homes. Some work for private agencies, and work in people's own homes. A few work for voluntary organisations, such as Macmillan Nurses, who look after cancer patients in the patient's own home.

Social workers (SWs) work mainly for social services departments (SSDs), but may be based at health centres or in hospitals as well as SSD offices. They may also be employed privately by doctors, but are more likely to be employed by the social services department and go to the surgery for a few hours a week to see people the doctor thinks have social problems.

Some social workers are employed by solicitors to help with work in the law courts, others work for voluntary organisations such as the National Society for the Prevention of Cruelty to Children (NSPCC) and Childline.

Other services may be available in the health centre at certain times, for example a dietitian may be there to give advice about food and eating on Monday afternoons between 2.30 pm and 4 pm, and a speech therapist in for one session every week.

Occupational therapists can be found working in the health service and in social services. They are often called 'OTs', and their job is to help people manage their day-to-day lives in a practical way. They will advise on how to do things better if you lose an arm, for instance. They also work out the best ways to change a house to suit somebody in a wheelchair, or who uses a walking frame. People with arthritis and some other illnesses cannot grip properly, so the OT will help them to find the aids they need to overcome the problem. These might be taps with long handles, or kettles which rock to pour the water out instead of having to be lifted up (see pages 148–9).

Another regular visitor may be the physiotherapist, often known as the 'physio'. They have had a three year training course to learn how to use exercise and manipulation, sometimes used with heat and electricity, to help people maintain as much movement as they can in their bodies. So after breaking a leg or an arm, or after having had a stroke, patients visit a physiotherapist to get rid of stiffness or other problems, and get their muscles and joints moving again.

Someone a doctor may send you to see (refer you to) is a radiographer. They are the people who take X-rays to see if any bones

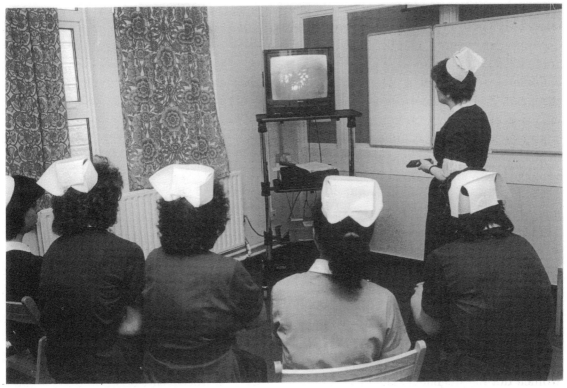

Figure 23   *Nurses study for three years*

are broken, or if there is anything inside you that should not be there. They also take a three-year training course, which includes a lot of science and physics to learn.

There may also be a medical secretary, who will do all the typing, filing, and making telephone calls to hospitals and other places for the GPs.

Self-check questions

1 Where do practice nurses work?
2 Name two things that practice nurses do.
3 Where do district nurses see their patients?
4 Which age group do health visitors do most of their work with?
5 What do midwives do?
6 What is the job of a medical secretary?
7 What would a dietician give you advice about?

DENTISTS

Dentists work to look after our teeth, but they also treat diseases, injuries and other conditions affecting the mouth and jaws. Many dentists work for the National Health Service, but more now have become self-employed, and treat only private patients. Dentists work in surgeries which can be found in all the larger towns. Some dentists work in hospitals, though, and in the bigger cities there are dental hospitals.

There is also a schools' dental service, which tries to prevent problems with children's teeth by regular checks and education about teeth and how to look after them for children at school. In a dentist's surgery, there will be a receptionist who does the same job as receptionists do for the doctors. There will also be dental surgery assistants or dental nurses who help the dentist in surgery while he is looking after teeth. They will pass the instruments and prepare the fillings to be put in, and do any dressings.

There may also be dental hygienists who will clean and polish teeth, and give advice on regular dental care and oral hygiene (keeping the mouth clean and fresh).

Dental technicians usually work in laboratories or workshops which serve an area with a lot of dentists. They are the people who make the false teeth, crowns and other bits and pieces a dentist might need.

Self-check questions

1 What does the schools' dental service do?
2 Can you remember seeing anyone from the schools' dental service when you were small?
3 If you can remember seeing them, what did they do for you?
4 What do dental nurses do?
5 What does a dental hygienist do?
6 What do dental technicians do?
7 How much does a dental check-up cost?
8 Working in pairs, count how many teeth you each have.

Student activity 4 (role play)

• Working in small groups, organise a short role play about going to the dentist. Decide who is going to be the dentist, who will be the nurse and who will be the receptionist, and how many patients there are. Not everybody needs to take part in the role play, but everybody in the group should take part in the planning. Each group should try to have something different in their play. You could start with somebody having really bad toothache, and wanting to be seen by a dentist quickly, or you could have a family going in for a routine check-up.
• Afterwards – is that what it is like when you go to the dentist? What is the worst part about a visit to the dentist? For the 'actors', how did it feel to be the dentist, or the dental nurse?

OPTICIANS

Your optician is concerned with eyesight, and prescribes and provides whatever is necessary to improve or correct it. Opticians do this by testing your eyes, and then prescribing glasses or contact lenses to correct any problems they have found. Opticians are also known as optometrists.

Most opticians work from shops which can be found usually in the high street of every town. Some work in hospitals or in factories. After the eyes have been tested, the optician will prescribe lenses for glasses or contact lenses which will help the person to see more clearly.

Examining the eyes sometimes shows up other diseases which an optician cannot treat (such as diabetes, or heart disease). When evidence of something like this is found, the patient will be sent to his/her own doctor

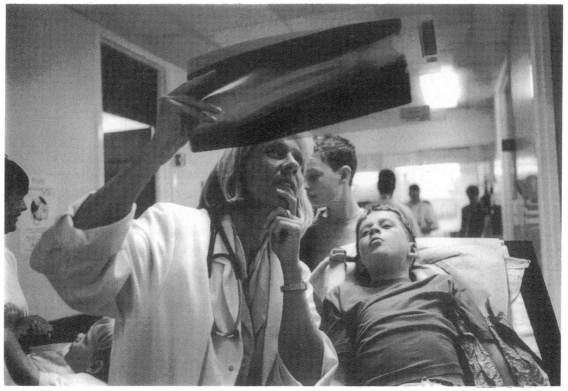

Figure 24   *Radiographers x-ray for broken bones*

with a letter describing what the optician has found.

This works the other way, too. Doctors send their patients to opticians when they think there is a problem that can be cured by the patient wearing glasses or contact lenses. Some people who have a lot of headaches may need glasses without realising it. The other people who work with the optician will act as receptionists and do the same job as receptionists for doctors and dentists. They will also help you choose frames for the prescribed lenses, and then adjust them so that they fit well. They can also give you advice on the different types of frames and glass or plastic lenses available, and on the different types of contact lenses.

Some of the work that opticians do is for the National Health Service (NHS), and some glasses are available on the NHS. Opticians also offer a full private service. Many people have an NHS eye test, and then buy their spectacles or contact lenses privately, as there is more choice in design and style.

Self-check questions

1 What does an optician do?
2 What is another name for an optician?
3 Where will an optician send you to if a disease is found during an eye test?
4 How will the staff at an opticians help you?
5 Why do people sometimes buy their glasses frame privately?

6 Where is your local optician?

7 Have you ever had an eye test?

8 What did you have to do when you had your eyes tested?

9 How much does an eye test cost?

Student activity 5

• Make your own eye test chart (you can copy the one in this book on to a big piece of paper), and test each other's eyesight.

• Hang the chart on a wall, and sit the person reading it about six paces away in front of it. Working in pairs, get your partner to cover one eye, and see how far they can read down the chart. Then cover the other eye and do the same thing again. After one person has done it, change over, and do the same thing yourself. If anyone wears glasses or contact lenses, get them to read the chart with and without them, if they don't mind.

HOSPITALS

As we have said before, hospitals are the largest health care institutions, so they need lots of different kinds of workers to keep them going, as shown in Figure 29 on page 69. Many are direct carers – the ones who look after the patients, but many more are 'indirect carers', the people who look after the carers, the buildings, and all the equipment.

We have already mentioned a couple of the indirect carers, the receptionist and the medical secretary. They also work in hospitals, and so do other people such as porters, administrators, maintenance and catering staff, and domestic assistants (see page 69).

Managers are in charge of the hospital and employ administrators to make sure that there are enough staff to do all the jobs and that there are the tools to do them. They are also responsible for making sure that everything is paid for, and that everyone working there gets their wages.

Clerical assistants work in the offices and in departments such as out-patients and admissions. They look after all the filing systems.

Domestic assistants make sure that everywhere is kept clean; porters transport and carry the things to where they are needed, deliver the meals, take away the rubbish, and move patients about from the wards to X-ray or physiotherapy, for instance.

The maintenance staff make sure that everything is kept in good repair and works properly. They are plumbers, electricians, and engineers, for example.

There is also a group of indirect carers who have moved on from being direct carers. There are managers and administrators who have done this. They started off as nurses and doctors, and then were promoted to jobs which did not bring them into direct contact with patients any more. Some of them work in offices, as mentioned, but others will have become teachers or advisors to all the other doctors and nurses or care professionals.

Student activity 6

• Find out what your teachers and lecturers did before they became teachers and lecturers.

• Find out how many of them were in direct caring jobs earlier in their lives.

• Are any of them still doing a caring job as well as a teaching job?

Figure 25   *Food delivered by*
meals on wheels service

Catering staff

Wherever there are people, there will have to be some sort of catering provided. Catering means providing the food. In hospitals, nursing homes, retirement homes, and many day centres, there are cooks and kitchen staff working. They have to provide, prepare, cook and serve the food for both the patients or clients, and often for the staff as well.

There are also cooks and drivers who work on 'meals on wheels' services, taking cooked meals to people in their own homes because they cannot manage to cook for themselves.

SOCIAL CARE

Since the introduction of the National Health Service and Community Care Act, there have been many more jobs for carers working in the community. More people are being looked after at home, so staff have to be employed to do that. This is one reason why there are more and more home care agencies being set up.

Home care agencies provide helpers to go into people's own houses and flats to do whatever the customer wants. This may be getting them up every morning and putting to bed at night. It may be bathing them once a week, or it may be providing a night sitter to stay all night long. The helper from the agency staff may be a well-qualified nurse, or a carer with no qualifications at all. It depends on what service has been asked for.

There is also always a demand for people to look after children, either in nurseries or playgroups, or in the children's own homes as nannies. Childminders also look after children, but the children have to go to the childminder's home.

Many of the staff in nurseries, playgroup leaders and some playgroup staff, nannies and childminders have either an NNEB (Nursery Nurses Examination Board) or a BTEC nursery nursing qualification, and some might have a National Vocational Qualification (NVQ) in child care. A qualification is not always needed to do these jobs.

Caring jobs can be found in schools, private retirement homes, nursing homes, with local authority housing departments, and with housing associations.

Housing departments run warden service housing schemes for elderly people. This might be using wardens who live in a house surrounded by elderly persons' bungalows or flats, and connected by alarm buttons, or it might be that the wardens are at a central control office, and there are telephone and computer links to all the elderly persons' houses. The elderly people can push a button on the telephone, or pull a cord hanging from the ceiling, or press an alarm button on a necklace to speak to the control centre. There is someone working at the control centre 24 hours a day, and other staff called 'mobile wardens' in cars or vans driving around to where they are wanted.

Housing associations provide housing for all sorts of people. They are often voluntary organisations, there to provide a public service and not to make a profit from it. Some housing associations will only provide housing for older people, some only for people with learning difficulties. Others only have accommodation for people who have been in prison, or who are recovering from a mental illness. Yet more only offer a service to single mothers, or women who have suffered from domestic violence (battered wives).

Self-check questions

1 What do the indirect carers do?
2 Name three indirect care jobs.
3 Name three types of office worker.
4 Name two types of maintenance staff.
5 What are meals on wheels?
6 Who prepares meals on wheels?
7 Housing associations are
   A local authority departments
   B voluntary organisations
   C Government departments?
8 Name two groups of people who may get help from housing associations.

See Appendix for answers.

Student activity 7

- Look at the selection of job advertisements in Figure 26 and see how many different jobs you can find.
- Look in your local paper and see what sort of caring jobs are advertised in there. Remember to keep evidence of your work for your portfolio.

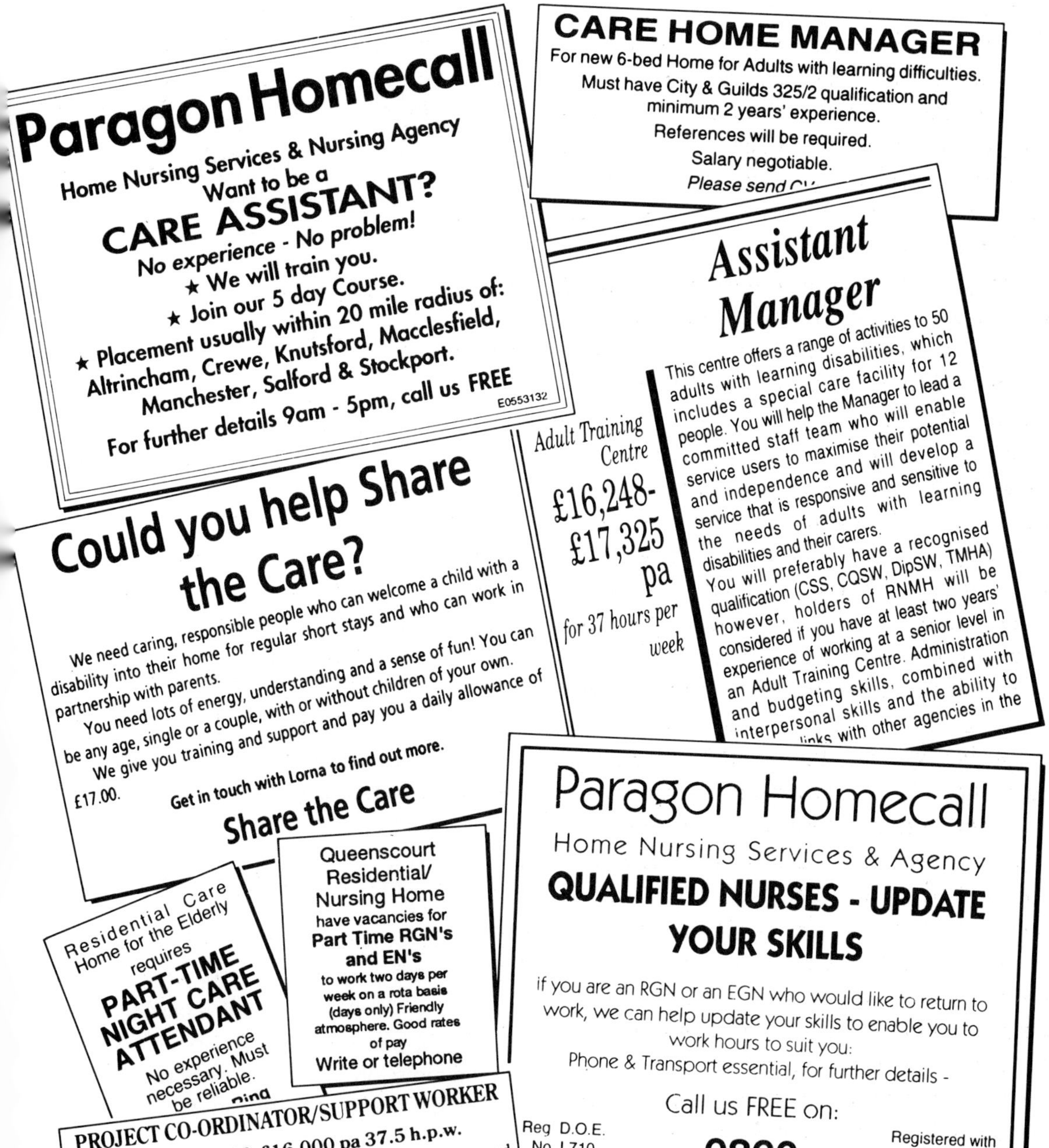

CARE HOME MANAGER

For new 6-bed Home for Adults with learning difficulties.
Must have City & Guilds 325/2 qualification and minimum 2 years' experience.
References will be required.
Salary negotiable.
Please send C...

Paragon Homecall

Home Nursing Services & Nursing Agency
Want to be a

CARE ASSISTANT?

No experience - No problem!
★ We will train you.
★ Join our 5 day Course.
★ Placement usually within 20 mile radius of:
Altrincham, Crewe, Knutsford, Macclesfield, Manchester, Salford & Stockport.

For further details 9am - 5pm, call us FREE

E0553132

Assistant Manager

Adult Training Centre

£16,248-£17,325 pa

for 37 hours per week

This centre offers a range of activities to 50 adults with learning disabilities, which includes a special care facility for 12 people. You will help the Manager to lead a committed staff team who will enable service users to maximise their potential and independence and will develop a service that is responsive and sensitive to the needs of adults with learning disabilities and their carers.

You will preferably have a recognised qualification (CSS, CQSW, DipSW, TMHA) however, holders of RNMH will be considered if you have at least two years' experience of working at a senior level in an Adult Training Centre. Administration and budgeting skills, combined with interpersonal skills and the ability to links with other agencies in the

Could you help Share the Care?

We need caring, responsible people who can welcome a child with a disability into their home for regular short stays and who can work in partnership with parents.

You need lots of energy, understanding and a sense of fun! You can be any age, single or a couple, with or without children of your own.

We give you training and support and pay you a daily allowance of £17.00.

Get in touch with Lorna to find out more.

Share the Care

Residential Care Home for the Elderly requires

PART-TIME NIGHT CARE ATTENDANT

No experience necessary. Must be reliable.
Ring

Queenscourt Residential/ Nursing Home have vacancies for
Part Time RGN's and EN's
to work two days per week on a rota basis (days only) Friendly atmosphere. Good rates of pay
Write or telephone

Paragon Homecall

Home Nursing Services & Agency

QUALIFIED NURSES - UPDATE YOUR SKILLS

if you are an RGN or an EGN who would like to return to work, we can help update your skills to enable you to work hours to suit you:
Phone & Transport essential, for further details -

Call us FREE on:

0800

Reg D.O.E.
No. L710

Registered with local authorities.
E0552620

PROJECT CO-ORDINATOR/SUPPORT WORKER

Salary £13,000-£16,000 pa 37.5 h.p.w.

This innovative project provides accommodation and continuing support for young single homeless people. The successful applicant will lead a small highly motivated staff team. Experience in the field is essential.

Figure 26   *Different types of job advertisements for carers*

ELEMENT 3.2

Investigate jobs in health and social care

At the end of this section, you should have

- identified two jobs in health and social care which are likely to suit you
- described the main purposes of each job identified
- explained why each job identified is likely to suit you
- identified the main skills required for each identified job
- identified the qualifications required for each identified job
- identified how to obtain skills and qualifications for each identified job
- learned how to seek advice and information from appropriate sources when necessary.

CHOOSING A JOB

Student activity 8

 • Now that you know about the many different kinds of jobs that there are in caring, which of them do you think you could do, and would like to do? The jobs may be direct care jobs (looking after people), or indirect care (looking after the carers or the buildings and equipment needed by the carers).

- Read through the information in the previous section again if you need to. Remind yourself about the different kinds of nurses, care assistants, social care workers, nannies, porters, office staff and maintenance workers.

- Choose the two which you like most, and write down the job titles. One should be a job that you can apply for when you have finished this course, the other should be one that you would like to do when you are more experienced or have more qualifications.

- For each one, answer the following questions.

    1 What is the purpose of the job, why is the job there? What do they have to do?
    2 Do you think you would be able to do the job, and why you would like to?

    3 What skills do you need for the job, including the core skills of application of number, communication and information technology?
    4 What qualifications would you need to get that job, how would you get on to a training course for it?

You should be able to get information about all these things from the library in your school or college, or the Careers Advice office.

- Look again at the job advertisements at the end of the previous section in this book. Look also at the advertisements in your local papers, and in the magazines for people from the caring sector, e.g. *Nursing Standard*, *Care Weekly*, *Community Care* and *Nursery World*, to see if there are any advertisements for the kind of jobs you are interested in.

    If you know of anybody doing the job already, you could ask them to tell you about it. If a few people in your group are interested in the same job, you could invite somebody who does the job to come in and speak to a group of you about it.

Student activity 9

 • Inviting a speaker. Decide who it is you would like to invite, either a person you know or somebody you do not know who is doing the job you are interested in. You could also invite somebody who can give advice on how to find jobs, such as a careers adviser. If you cannot think of anyone, ask your tutors for help.

Find out from your tutors when would be the best time to ask somebody to come in – not just the day of the week, but the best time of day as well.

When you have decided who it is you will be inviting, one of you will have to ring them up and ask them if they will come and talk to you. If they will, check which day they will be free, and if the time your tutor gave you is suitable for them. If they are not able to come, ask if they know anybody who can, and then speak to that person. (It is a good idea to ask now if there will be any charge for them coming to speak, and telling your tutor if there is before you do anything else.)

When you have found somebody to come, you will have to write them a letter (using a word-processor) confirming the dates and times. You should also ask them if they will want anything for the talk, such as an overhead projector, or a flip-chart. Use school or college headed paper for your letter, and have it checked by your tutor before you send it out.

On the day of the talk, two of your group should meet your guest when they arrive, and show them to the room. You could also show them where the toilet is, and ask if they want a drink of tea or coffee. Do not forget to introduce them to your tutor.

After the talk, remember to thank them for their time, and make sure that one of you shows them the way out. They may not know their way around as well as you do. Write a letter of thanks to be sent afterwards.

If more than one speaker is wanted, you can do the same thing over again for them, but share the work out so that everybody has a chance to share in organising the visits.

- Write about your involvement in the organisation of the visit, and use this in your portfolio of core skills.

Writing the letters for this section will give you evidence towards core skills (Communications 1.3, and Information Technology 1.3 if you use a word-processor).

More information on how to go about finding a job is in the next section of this book.

Plan for employment in health and social care

At the end of this section, you should have

- produced your own curriculum vitae
- described the main ways to find out about job vacancies in health and social care
- described the main stages of recruitment in health and social care
- described different ways of presenting personal information to prospective employers
- know where to seek advice and information about jobs and job applications in health and social care.

CURRICULUM VITAE

Do not let the words put you off. A curriculum vitae (or CV) is just a record of your life so far. If you have been keeping a record of achievement (ROA) from school, this will be a part of your CV.

The difference between a CV and a life story is that in a CV you pick out the parts that are important for a particular purpose. So if you are applying for a job working with children, you concentrate on your experience of looking after children. This may be babysitting, or looking after your own younger brothers and sisters, or any job you might have had – whether it was paid or not – where you were looking after children. You will need a CV because many employers will ask you for one whenever you apply for a job.

Student activity 10

- Putting a CV together. Start by making some basic notes about yourself and your life. Begin with your name and date of birth, and where you live at the moment. Also mention whether you are single, married, divorced or widowed, and whether or not you have children. After that it is easiest to go through your life from the beginning.

  Write down a few notes about your family – who is in it? Have you any brothers or sisters? Are they older or younger than you? Can you remember if you went to any playgroups or nurseries? Which primary and junior schools did you go to? Which secondary schools did you attend? Did you pass any exams there (GCSEs, A Levels, or any other)? Have you had any jobs? Think of Saturday jobs, evening jobs, newspaper rounds, babysitting, or anything else whether it was paid or unpaid.

What are you good at? What do you not like doing? Are you in, or have you ever been in any clubs or groups such as Scouts, Guides, Brownies, Cubs, churches, youth clubs, athletics clubs, swimming clubs, etc? What are your hobbies? What do you do in your spare time?

What are you studying or working at now? What would you like to do next? And after that?

These notes can now be used to write a proper CV which you can keep up to date, and use whenever you apply for a job, or perhaps another course.

The real thing

If possible, keep your CV on a computer disk, as it is easier to change it when you need to, and print off as many as you need without all the hard work of writing it out again and again. This will also give you evidence towards all elements of core skills in information technology at Level 1.

When you are writing out the final version of your CV, using a lot of different headings makes it easier for you to write, and easier for other people to read.

Below are some suggested headings which should be suitable for most applications, but you may need to put some others in or leave things out depending on what you are going to use the CV for. Always start with the basic information.

- Full name
- Address and telephone number
- Date of birth
- Nationality and the town where you were born
- Marital status   (As we have said above, this is whether you are single, married, divorced, living with someone, widowed, and whether you have children or not.)

- Education record (Put down here all the schools you have been to, and the dates when you started and when you left.)
- Qualifications (Leave this out if you have none, or put in any GCSEs, City and Guilds, BTEC or any other qualifications you have, and the year that you got them.)
- Awards (If you have any awards for swimming, athletics, playing a musical instrument, or for bravery, or Duke of Edinburgh's award, etc. then mention them here.)
- Employment record (Put here any jobs you have had, and the dates when you started and when you finished.)
- Current employment (Only to be used when you actually have a job at the time you are writing, it may be part-time, full-time, paid or voluntary job.)
- Hobbies and interests (Put down here what you do in your own time.)
- Referees (When you apply for jobs, and sometimes for courses, you will be asked to give the names and addresses of two referees who know you. One should know you from work, school or college, the other can be a friend. Always ask them if it is alright to put their names down as referees.)

Figure 27 shows an example of how a completed Curriculum Vitae may look.

Student activity 11

- To help you think about what you are good at, and what you may need some help with, answer the questions in the right hand column and on pages 61–63 by ticking the one out of each four which you think most applies to you. Try to be honest about your answers.

Listening and Attending	Tick a box
1. I am very good at listening to others and usually give them my full attention.	
2. I can listen fairly well but I am easily distracted.	
3. I find listening to people difficult and prefer talking.	
4. I am not very good at listening at all.	

Talking: Giving Information	Tick a box
1. I usually give appropriate and clear information.	
2. I give as much information as possible whenever I can.	
3. I like to assess what information people want before I offer it.	
4. I don't particularly like giving information to people.	

Curriculum Vitae for J. Shields

FULL NAME:	Jennifer Anne Shields
ADDRESS:	16 Wentworth Close
	Lestall
	Wennockshire
	ZS2 9US
TELEPHONE:	01836 923814
DATE OF BIRTH:	25.4.78
NATIONALITY:	British
MARITAL STATUS:	Single, no children
EDUCATION RECORD:	Lockton St. Primary School, Sealford 1983–86
	Lestall Junior School 1986–89
	Heelby Comprehensive School 1989–94
	Heelby College of Further Education 1994–present
QUALIFICATIONS:	GCSEs in English Grade C
	Maths Grade D
	Home Economics Grade B
AWARDS:	First Aid Certificate from Red Cross
	Lifesavers Badge for Swimming
	BAGA Award for Gymnastics
	Ballet Certificate
EMPLOYMENT:	Newspaper deliveries 1992–93
	Fruit picking in summer holidays
	Babysitting for people in Sealford
	Waitress in Lestall Arms 1993–present
HOBBIES/INTERESTS:	Sports (in netball and rounders teams)
	Going to discos
	Watching television and videos
	Helping at Brownies

REFEREES:	Mr M. Winton	Miss T. Hall
	Heelby Comprehensive	Briar Patch
	Heelby	Lestall Lane
	Wennockshire	Lestall
	HL6 5MN	Wennockshire
		ZS2 9YG

Figure 27   *A sample curriculum vitae*

Talking: Supporting	Tick a box
1. I am usually very supportive of other people.	
2. I can support people but have my limits.	
3. I prefer other people to be supportive.	
4. Trying to be supportive makes me anxious and I am not very good at it.	

Talking: Confronting	Tick a box
1. I can confront effectively when I need to.	
2. I tend to be more aggressive than confronting.	
3. I tend to be more submissive than confronting.	
4. I don't like confronting people at all.	

Talking: Drawing Out	Tick a box
1. I can draw people out fairly easily and enjoy doing it.	
2. I can sometimes draw people out but I don't often achieve it.	
3. I find drawing people out difficult.	
4. I try to avoid drawing people out.	

Talking: Coping with Emotions	Tick a box
1. I cope with other peoples' emotion well.	
2. I can cope if someone cries but I don't feel very comfortable.	
3. I would call someone to help if someone started to cry.	
4. I do not like coping with other peoples' emotions at all.	

Opening a Conversation	Tick a box
1. I can start conversations very easily.	
2. I can start a conversation with some difficulty.	
3. I try to let the other person start the conversation.	
4. I find the whole topic very difficult.	

Structuring a Conversation	Tick a box
1. I find it easy to control and structure a conversation.	
2. I do not normally think about structuring.	
3. I usually leave the structuring of a conversation to the other person.	
4. I prefer to be 'natural' in a conversation.	

Ending a Conversation	Tick a box
1. I can usually end a conversation quite easily.	
2. I often find it difficult to end conversations.	
3. I usually wait till the other person finishes the conversation.	
4. I find ending conversations very difficult.	

Working in Groups	Tick a box
1. I enjoy group work and find no difficulty in working with groups.	
2. I am sometimes unsure what to say in group meetings.	
3. I would rather not work in groups.	
4. I try to avoid groups.	

Running Groups	Tick a box
1. I would enjoy chairing or facilitating a group meeting.	
2. I think I could run a group if I was asked to.	
3. I would feel very uncomfortable if I was asked to run a group.	
4. I could not run a group.	

Being Assertive	Tick a box
1. I think I am assertive.	
2. I am more aggressive than assertive.	
3. I am more submissive than assertive.	
4. I am not sure whether or not I am assertive.	

Writing Skills	Tick a box
1. I write fairly clearly and well.	
2. I need to improve my writing skills.	
3. I do not write well.	
4. I try to avoid putting things in writing.	

Computing Skills	Tick a box
1. I am quite happy using computers of different sorts.	
2. I can use a computer but not very easily.	
3. I don't know much about computers.	
4. I avoid computers if possible.	

Self-Awareness	Tick a box
1. I think I know myself reasonably well.	
2. I need to get to know myself better.	
3. I am often surprised by the things that I do.	
4. I don't think I know myself at all.	

- Once you have worked through these boxes, discuss your findings with other members of your group. See what they

think of your answers. Getting feedback from others is useful for assessing yourself.

Burnard, P. (1992)

FINDING JOBS

When you finish your training courses and are looking for a job, what do you have to do?

First you need to decide what type of job you are interested in, which you have done for Element 3.2. You may have changed your mind since the time you did that and the time you are looking for a job, though. This is fine, we are all allowed to change our minds.

The next decision you may want to make is whether to go for a paid job or for a voluntary job. If you cannot get a paid job, it is sometimes worth considering a voluntary job so that you can get experience, and this will help you to get a paid job later. We will start first with voluntary jobs.

Voluntary jobs

There are opportunities for doing voluntary work locally, nationally and abroad.

Locally, you should look in the local newspaper and in the telephone book to see if there is a council of voluntary service or similar organisation. They are the place that all the small voluntary groups use to recruit volunteers.

They may want people to help do the shopping for people who are housebound, or babysitting and grannysitting services to allow the regular carers to get out now and again. Another one might be helping them to get money, so collecting on flag days or working in a charity shop could be something you could help with.

Look at the notice boards around your school or college, there may be posters asking for voluntary help. A good organisation to get in touch with if you really want to move about and get some really interesting experience is CSV, or Community Service Volunteers. They are at 237 Pentonville Road, London N1 9NJ, telephone 0171 278 6601.

The Volunteer Centre UK will also give information about volunteering. They are at 29 Lower Kings Road, Berkhampstead, Herts HP24 2AB, telephone 01442 773311.

For more adventurous people, there are places that will help you work in other countries. Bunacamp and CampAmerica take people to work with children every year at US summer camps. Look for their advertisements in newspapers and magazines.

Voluntary Services Overseas (VSO) are often looking for people to work all over the world, although usually they want people with qualifications to do specialist jobs. You can contact them at VSO, 317 Putney Bridge Road, London SW15, telephone 0171 937 7770.

Paid jobs

When you are ready to look for a paid job, there are still decisions to be made. What type of work are you interested in? Even in health and social care there are lots of different types of work to do. As you have learned earlier in this chapter, there is either direct work looking after people, or indirect work looking after the buildings and the equipment needed by the direct workers.

If you are interested in direct work, what sort of people would you like to be helping?

Do you prefer looking after older people or children? Mentally ill people, those with learning difficulties or people with a physical disability? There are other groups, but these are the main ones.

Next you will have to decide whether you are able to work part time or full time, and whether you could work shifts or nights or prefer just 9 am to 5 pm.

Where to look

So where can you find out about what jobs are available? One of the easiest things to do is get hold of a local newspaper. If you do not want to buy one, you can look at one free in the library. Remember to take some paper and a pen to write down any jobs you find which you want to apply for.

Some national newspapers also have job advertisement pages, but these are usually in other towns. If you want to leave home, you can look at these. Some of them may give you somewhere to live with the job. For others you will have to find somewhere to live yourself. Read the advertisements carefully so that you know what you are applying for.

Another good place to find out about work is at a Job Centre. There is one of these in each town. You should find out where the nearest one is today. You can go in to these every day and look at the cards displayed to see if there is anything you would be interested in. You can also speak to an adviser if you want some help. They can also put your name on a list, and let you know if any types of jobs you want to know about come in.

If you are more interested in indirect work, you may be looking at advertisements for domestic staff, cooks, laundry workers, drivers, maintenance staff, etc. Magazines are also a good source of health and social care job vacancies. The specialist ones such as *Nursing Standard, Care Weekly, Nursery World* and *Community Care* have a wide choice every week.

In your own local area, do not forget to look in the shop windows where postcards are put advertising all sorts of things. You could find child-care jobs, or jobs looking after older people advertised here, and they will probably be quite near to where you live.

You could also ask anybody that you know who works in health and social care if they know of any jobs you might be able to apply for. There is nothing to stop you getting in touch with any places that you know and asking if there is a vacancy. So a letter or 'phone call to your local hospital or retirement homes or nurseries could get you work.

Agencies are a bit like the Job Centres, but they are private rather than a government office. There are a lot of these around the towns and cities, but fewer in the countryside. They need people to work on what are often short-term contracts looking after people in their own homes, or sometimes in nursing homes, retirement homes or hospitals where they are short of regular staff. There are also agencies which specialise in finding work for nannies and nursery nurses, and you do not always need a qualification.

For general advice, there may be a careers adviser in your school or college. If there is not, they will be able to make an appointment for you with one in the area.

What happens next?

After you have found the job you are interested in, what do you do next? Read the advertisement, if that is how you found out about it. It may say to write in or to tele-phone for an application form. It may say that you should send in your CV with a letter saying why you are interested in the job. More often than not you will let them know that you are interested by 'phone or by letter, and they will send you an application form to fill in.

Fill it in the best way you can (this will also give you evidence toward Communications Core Skills at Level 1) you may be able to send your CV off with it if you are asked about your background and interests.

It is a good idea to take a photocopy of application forms before you fill them in, and use this spare copy for practice (writing in pencil so that you can rub out mistakes) and to keep for yourself when you send the real one off in the post. Make sure you send everything off by the date it says in the advertisement, or on the letter or application form.

Once the place advertising the job has all the applications in, they will decide who to invite for an interview. What you have put on your application form helps them to decide who to invite.

Job interviews

If you are one of the few people invited to attend for an interview, you know that the information you put on to your application form or into your CV got you there.

So what do you need to do to prepare for a job interview? First, you should read through all the information you have available. The advertisement you first saw, the letter and job description that came with the application form, and any information you have had over the telephone or from other people who work there, if you have spoken to any.

Second, it is a good idea to go to the place where you will be interviewed, and to the place where you will be working (if it is different) to check how to get there, and how long it will take you.

Third, think about the questions you are likely to be asked, and what your answers are going to be. You should also think about any questions you want to ask them. It is a good idea to write these down on a piece of paper, and keep it in your pocket. You will be nervous when you are interviewed, and may not remember what you were going to ask without your note to remind you. Do not just ask about the money or the holidays as this gives a bad impression.

Finally, decide what you are going to wear. Remember that you are not going to a disco or to college, but to a job interview where it is important that you make a good impression.

There are usually two or three people on an interview panel, it will rarely be you with just one other person.

Some common questions

Job interviews normally start with a few words about how you are, how was your journey, the weather, and so on. When you get to the real business, there are certain questions which have to be asked, but not always in the same way.

- Why have you applied for this job?
- Have you any experience of this kind of work?
- Tell us about what qualifications you have (or what course you are on).

- What qualities and skills do you have that would help you in this job?
- What sort of things are you good at? (Sometimes, what are your worst subjects at school or college?)
- Questions about the job, and what you may do in certain situations e.g. 'If you found Mrs Smith had fallen out of bed, what would you do?'. 'We have a no smoking policy in this building, if Mr Jones wanted a smoke, how would you deal with it?'
- How will you manage with getting here for 8 am working shifts?
- Have you any questions you would like to ask us?

Sometimes straight after an interview you will be told whether you have got the job or not. Usually you will have to wait a while, as there will be more people to interview after you. Then you may have either a 'phone call or a letter (sometimes both) to tell you if you have got the job or not.

Student activity 12

- Use the job description printed earlier and get everybody in your group to apply for it. In two groups, go through the applications and see who you would invite to an interview. For those who did not get invited, tell them why (in writing), and get them to apply again.
- Group A will look at the applications from group B, and group B will look at the applications from group A.
- When all the applications are satisfactory, set up your interview panels of three people each, and interview the job applicants from the other group. Make sure that everybody has a turn on the interview panel, and that everybody is interviewed. Taking part in the

Figure 28   *Interviews are normally carried out by a panel*

interview will give you evidence towards Core Skills in Communication at Level 1.1.

- After the interview, the panel should give feedback to the person they have just interviewed. Did they come across well? Have they given them the job? Did they answer the questions clearly and fully? How could they do better?

Self-check questions

1   What do the letters CV stand for?
2   What will you need a CV for?

3   How should you start putting a CV together?
4   Why is it best to keep your CV on a computer disk?
5   Why is it worth considering voluntary jobs?
6   Name an organisation which will help you with information about voluntary jobs.
7   Name three places where you can find out about jobs in health and social care.
8   Why should you copy job application forms?
9   Write down two things you should do before going for a job interview.
10 What are two questions commonly asked at job interviews?

And what about the rewards at the end of the week or month? Out of your wages all the expenses have to be paid, including travelling to work, eating, buying clothes and paying rent. This links in with some of the work for Chapter 2.

Reference
Burnard, P. (1992) *Communicate!* London: Edward Arnold.

4

CONTRIBUTING TO A TEAM ACTIVITY

Whenever and wherever you may work in health and social care, you will usually be a part of a team. The team may not all be there at the same time, but it is still a team. Home carers (home helps), for example, work individually in their clients' homes, but they are still part of a home care team. It is the same in hospitals, the night staff are still a part of the caring team, even if they only meet the day staff for a short period at the beginning and end of shifts.

So being able to work as part of a team is important, there will always be times when you have to rely on other people, and when other people are relying on you. How would you, your teachers and lecturers manage if your college was not kept clean, warm and tidy, if the equipment was not there and in working order when it was needed?

It is just the same working in health and social care settings. A team of people working together is needed to provide any of the services required.

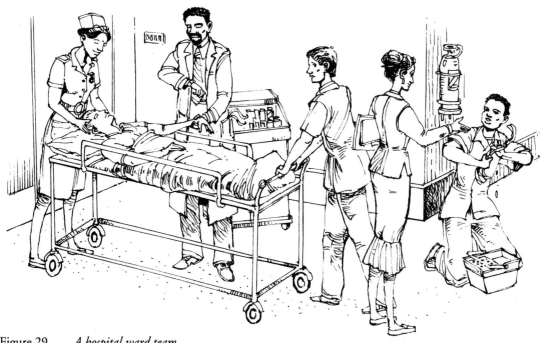

Figure 29   *A hospital ward team*

ELEMENT 4.1

Plan an activity with a team

The first thing you will have to do is decide what activity you want to be involved in.

Next you should check that you and all the other members of the team understand what you want to get from the activity. The team will then have to agree on what needs to be done.

Start by looking at what is available for you to use. These are known as the resources, and include such things as how many people there are, what rooms or fields you could use, how much time you have, and how much money you can get, plus anything else that you may need to use. Make sure that every team member takes part in this discussion.

The next important job is to decide who will be doing what, and that everybody has something to do. You should also look at what might go wrong, and how the team will deal with any problems. The team will also have to make sure that nobody is in any danger at any time. If you are to use any equipment, make sure that you know how to use it properly. Do not stand on chairs or tables – get a pair of stepladders. If your activity is to be outside at night, wear reflective clothing. Look closely at what you decide to do, and think of the safety measures which need to be taken.

Elect one of your group to keep a written record of all this, and then make enough copies for everybody to have one to keep in their file. Using a computer disk can make this a much easier job, and gives the writer evidence towards their core skills in information technology and communication. You should also keep a record of your own part in the planning, of what contributions you have made.

One of the easiest ways to do all this is to keep a notebook, and jot down in it what you have done and agreed to do next after each meeting, or after each piece of work involved with the activity.

At the end of this section, you should have records for your portfolio which show that you have

- checked that you have an accurate understanding of the given objectives of the activity
- agreed actions which will meet the overall objectives
- contributed to identifying the resources which are available
- contributed to identifying which team members are going to carry out different parts of the activity
- contributed to identifying actions to deal with anticipated problems and maintained health and safety
- contributed to producing a realistic team plan for the overall activity
- agreed and produced a realistic individual plan which provides details of your own role in the activity.

IDEAS FOR ACTIVITIES

So what sort of team activities can you do? What about organising a party? This may be for small children, could be a Christmas, Easter, halloween, or birthday party. It could be a lunch for older people at a day centre or social club, or an entertainment of some sort for those living in a residential home. Perhaps a party for people with learning difficulties who attend your college? Or even a party for yourselves at the end of term, or for Christmas, or the end of the course?

Objectives

So what are the objectives of this particular activity? That is, what do you want to do? Make people happy, take them out, teach them something they did not know before? At the very least, a safe and successful party and one which gives you the evidence to achieve this unit.

Actions

What will the team have to do to organise the party? Having decided who the party will be for, you will next need to decide when and where, then get permission for that. This can only be done when you know the details.

Figure 30   *You could organise a party*

If it is at the school or college, you will need to get permission from there. If it is to be somewhere else, you will have to find out who to contact. How much money will you need? Where will it come from? Will you have to pay to use the room? What will you need to get? Make a list divided into what you need to buy and what you can borrow or get for free. Invitations and envelopes need to be on the list or posters to advertise your party. Design these and use the evidence toward your core skills.

Food and drinks, plates, cups, table cloths – will you need knives, forks and spoons, or will there only be sandwiches and cakes which people can eat with their fingers? What about rubbish bags and things for cleaning up afterwards? Will there be any organised games? What will you need for these? Who is going to do what?

These are only ideas to get you started, you will have to discuss with your tutor or teacher the details of your particular party.

Another idea is an outing. This can be - for groups such as the ones mentioned above in the party idea. Decide who you will invite, and where you would like to take them. Then look at days when it could be done to suit everybody. Some points to consider are

- which day of the week would be most suitable
- the times of day for the outing to begin and end
- the distance you will be travelling
- how you will get everybody there and back
- how much it is all going to cost
- where the money is going to come from
- what arrangements need to be made for food (does anybody need a special diet?).

Once again, these are only ideas to start you off. Your tutor or teacher will advise on the details.

You might have to do some fundraising to raise money for your party or your outing, but this can be an activity in its own right. First you must decide who you are going to raise funds for. There are many voluntary organisations which need money, and will help you with advice and guidance on how to do it. One of these is the Winged Fellowship Trust, which provides holidays for disabled people. They may be contacted at Winged Fellowship Trust, Angel House, 20–32 Pentonville Road, London N1 9XD. The following points are from WFT guidelines on fundraising, and are reproduced with their kind permission.

HOW TO ORGANISE A FUNDRAISING EVENT

Considerations

1 Previous experience

Have you ever run a similar event before? If not, and you know of anyone who has, it may be useful to ask their advice.

2 Steps to take?

What steps do you need to take to run the event? It is always helpful to make a plan, with dates. For example, if running a quiz and buffet evening, the steps might be

Step	Date
Decide on a date and get some friends committed to help you on the day!	
Organise venue/time etc.	23 October
Get tickets printed	25 October
Send out tickets for selling	1 November
Publicise the event	2 November
Ring round to check numbers	26 November
Buy provisions	28 November
Organise tables, chairs etc.	29 November
Brief everyone helping at event	30 November

3   Can you run the event on your own?

If not, you need to gather together a group of helpers and give them all specific tasks so that they know exactly what they are expected to do. Find out their interests and talents and maximise them as much as possible, as people enjoy doing things they are good at or interested in.

4   Budget

Budget checklist   It is useful to work out how much you will have to spend when running an event. You could use this sheet as a checklist and jot down how much each item will cost. This might include

Printing
Tickets
Sponsor forms
Leaflets
Posters
Invitations

Photography
Films
Batteries

Provisions
Food
Drink

Hire of equipment
Chairs/tables
Room hire
Video
Public announcement system

Prizes
Raffle or other (if possible get as many prizes donated as you can)

However, many events are put on specifically for the purpose of publicity and therefore whatever is raised is a bonus. It is important to keep costs to a minimum and if you can manage to get anything sponsored or donated this will help the overall profit potential of the event.

5   Tickets and sponsor forms

If it is a ticketed or sponsored event make sure that tickets are sold and sponsor forms sent out well in advance. Be sure that the legal requirements are complied with. If in doubt, ask someone who works for the charity you are fundraising for, or your local police, as they will be able to advise you.

6   Publicity

You can get lists of local media contacts from your local library, e.g. radio, local papers, local 'what's on' publications.

Special considerations

Make sure that whatever you do is
   A) safe
   B) legal
   C) cost effective
   D) fun!!

Figure 31   *Organising a fundraising event – guidelines from the Winged Fellowship Trust*

Apart from going around with a tin asking for people to put money into it, there are many sponsored things which can be done, such as sponsored walks, sponsored clean-ups, horse rides, swims, pancake races, etc.

Decide who you want to raise the money for. Make contact with them and ask for their advice. They may even send a speaker to tell you about how to do it.

Course visits can be arranged as a team activity. Where would you want to visit? A hospital? A special school? A hostel or sheltered housing complex? A careers exhibition? Consider the same points as you need to for the other suggestions – which day, what times, how many people, transport, costs, catering and so on. And work closely with your teacher or tutor at all times.

What might go wrong?

What if you have planned an outdoor event, and the weather is awful? You will need to make plans to cover this, either to hold the event indoors, or to change to something else which can be done indoors. Possibly even an alternative date.

Think about problems that could occur, like people turning up late, transport breaking down, and people getting lost or injured. Have a plan ready so that everybody knows what to do if any of these things, or others that you can think of, should happen. If it is at all possible, it is a very good idea to video the activity, and then use this in the review of your work in Element 4.3. You could also take photographs to put into your own portfolio. For some activities, an audio tape may be appropriate.

Remember you should be able to cover a lot of the core skills in this activity, but exactly which ones will depend on what you take part in, and what you do towards it. Discuss this with your tutor/teacher, and include core skills in your personal action plan.

Figure 32   *Plan for what can go wrong*

SUGGESTED TEAM ACTIVITY

The following team activity links with Element 3.1, and will give you some portfolio evidence for Element 1.1.

Student activity I

- If you can use a kitchen, why not plan and cook a healthy meal as a group?
- Decide what the meal is going to be and when you will be having it, and what each person is going to do to help with the preparation.
- Write down what your job will be, and how you are going to do it. Keep a record of what you do, and when you did it. (You could use your diary to do this.)

- Now you know what the meal will be, you can work out how much it is going to cost. How much of each food you will need depends on how many people will be eating the meal. When the cost has been worked out, you will know how much it will cost for each person (divide the cost by the number of people).
- Where is the money coming from? Will your school/college provide it? Will you collect it from each of the people who will be eating? Or will you organise an event to make the money needed, such as a raffle in the college?
- What pots and pans will you need? Are they in the kitchen you will be using or will you need to borrow anything?
- A shopping trip will have to be made, where is the cheapest place that any of you know about?
- Make sure that you follow all the rules for safety when using the kitchen.

Remember that you should be able to cover a lot of the core skills in this activity, but exactly which ones will depend on what you take part in, and what you do towards it.

Discuss this with your tutor/teacher, and include core skills in your personal action plan.

ELEMENT 4.2

Undertake a role in a team activity

In order to build up the evidence you need for your portfolio, you will need to show that you have

- followed the activities in the agreed individual plan and the agreed team plan
- made the best use of available resources
- maintained health and safety
- co-operated effectively with others as required by the plans
- responded to problems promptly and in the correct way.

EVIDENCE

You will need a copy of the overall plan which was completed by the person elected to keep notes for you during the meetings when everything was being planned. If you were that person, you should make sure that everybody has a copy and agrees with what you have put in it.

When it was decided who would be doing what to help toward the event, that is your individual plan. You should make sure that you write down what you have agreed to do, and how you are going to do it. So if you are going to make 'phone calls and write letters, you should plan in advance who you are going to telephone and write to, about what, and when. If you have to book a room, for instance, it is no good inviting anybody until you know if it is free when you want it. So the order in which things have to be done is an important part of planning.

Explain why you have done things the way that you have, and why this was the best way to use your time and other resources. Explain how you will make sure everybody is safe, both for your part in the activity and the activity as a whole.

Write something about how you worked with the other members of the team, and how you decided who would be doing what. Also keep a record of how you will deal with any problems that might come up, and who you will work with to deal with them. Remember to record any core skills which you use.

As a part of the evidence for this Element, you will need to have one of the tutors/teachers observing what you are doing toward this activity. Find out which member of staff it is, and that they know your plan of action and plans to deal with any problems before you start.

If you are going to take any videos, photographs or tape recordings, check that you have everything you need, including spare film and tapes and that the equipment is working properly.

Figure 33   *Have trained help on hand*

ELEMENT 4.3

Review the activity

Now that all the excitement and enjoyable activity is over, it is time to look at how things went; so you will have to

- review the extent to which the overall objectives were met
- review the use of resources
- review whether responses to problems were effective
- review maintenance of health and safety

- provide clear and constructive feedback to others on their performance
- respond constructively to feedback from others
- make and record suggestions for improvements in the way similar activities are tackled in the future.

If you were able to take a video of the activity, you can use this as an aid to reviewing it now.

Self-check questions

1 Did I do what I said I would do?
2 Did I manage to do it in the way I set out to do it?

3 Were the other members of the team doing what they said they would do?
4 Were the team's goals achieved?
5 Did each member achieve their own goal?

The team should get together for a group

discussion, without anybody becoming too angry, and look at each other's performance. If there is any praise to be given, then give it. If some criticism is needed, then make it constructive criticism, including looking at the reasons why something was or was not done, and how things could be changed to avoid these problems next time.

Team-check questions

1 Were people given the tasks most suited to their abilities and interests?
2 Were the materials and equipment used the most appropriate, and used in the best way?
3 How long did the whole thing take? Could

this time be reduced, or was more needed? Why?
4 How did the exercise seem to the observers, your teacher or lecturer? Make sure that you get their views on the assignment as a whole, and on your individual performance.
5 Was it a safe exercise? Were all the health and safety requirements taken into account?
6 Did any accidents happen? Why? How were they dealt with?

Student activity 2

Write, tape record or video a short piece for your portfolio on how you think you would do things differently if you could do this activity again, including comments on all the points mentioned above.

5

INVESTIGATING COMMON HEALTH EMERGENCIES

This optional unit makes you aware of the possible dangers which can occur in a place where people are cared for, how to reduce the chances of an accident or emergency happening and what to do if you are involved in an emergency situation.

ELEMENT 5.1

Investigate key health and safety factors in care settings

At the end of this section you should have

- identified and provided examples of common hazards in care settings
- identified safety equipment and ways of reducing safety risks to clients in care settings
- identified the main responsibilities of an employer and employees regarding health and safety regulations in care settings
- described the benefits to individuals of following health and safety regulations.

Care settings include any form of residential establishment, nursery or playgroup, hospital or the client's own home.

COMMON HAZARDS AND WAYS OF REDUCING RISKS

Fire

In care settings there are often many clients who are physically unable to help themselves, unable to read or follow instructions, ill, unconscious, confused or disorientated. They are more exposed to danger than other people who can remove themselves from the hazard or take steps to deal with it. It is very important that care workers at all levels help to prevent accidents by recognising unsafe conditions and equipment.

Learning about fire safety is part of everyone's job. Each person must know how to prevent fires, sound alarms, or if appropriate remove clients and fight small fires. Most fires are caused by careless handling of tobacco products, particularly cigarettes. Fortunately, many hospitals and other care premises are becoming no smoking areas, but this also may mean people who ignore the regulations and put out cigarettes quickly may not do so properly.

To reduce the danger of fires from smoking

- make sure people obey the rules about smoking
- make sure people only smoke in the places set aside for smoking
- provide proper ashtrays which are emptied at regular intervals, making sure that all stubs are dead and ashes are cold
- supervise clients with learning difficulties and those who are confused or forgetful who smoke.

All this means that you must know the rules about smoking in a place where you work or learn.

Student activity 1

- Find out the policy on smoking in your school, college or preferably workplace and conduct a survey among your peers to find out how much they know about it. Analyse your results to find out whether more publicity should be given to the policy. You could do this on your own or in a group to cover more individuals being surveyed. (Core skills Application of Number 1.1, 1.2.)

Electrical equipment must be checked regularly because it can cause a fire if it is not used properly or if it is in bad condition.

To reduce the danger of fires from incorrect use or poor condition of electrical equipment

- make sure flexes (wires) run in safe places and are correctly fastened down e.g. not under carpets, trailing across floors

- do not have too many plugs in sockets and adaptors – clients' homes are particular risks
- regularly check flexes for frayed, cracked or broken insulation – clients' homes are particularly vulnerable
- never attempt to correct electrical faults yourself – call a qualified electrician to do this
- remember flexes you cannot see such as electric blankets
- electrical equipment belonging to the care establishment and the client's personal appliances should be checked.

Many care premises have clients who require oxygen from cylinders to help them with breathing from time to time. Oxygen in cylinders is under pressure and can cause explosions or make an existing fire much worse. To reduce the danger from pressurised oxygen in cylinders

- always make sure the cylinders are stored in proper storage areas with caps on their valves
- use only special electrical safe equipment in places where oxygen is used
- never allow anyone to smoke where oxygen is used or stored
- put notices up when oxygen is used so other people know
- make sure that an authorised person (someone who has been trained to do the job) tests all the equipment used with an oxygen cylinder regularly to test for leaks.

Many other materials may also, if used carelessly, cause explosions or catch fire. They are called inflammable or flammable substances and should be clearly labelled. Many of the materials used in cleaning and routine maintenance are inflammables.

Figure 34 *Call a qualified person*

To reduce the danger from inflammable materials you should

 • store inflammables in safe clearly-labelled areas
• store materials away from heat sources
• never allow anyone to smoke around inflammable materials.

 To reduce the risk of inflammables causing fire, you need to know how to recognise the labels of inflammable substances.

Student activity 2

 • Ask a health and safety officer, fire person or other suitably trained person to give your group a short talk on recognising and dealing with inflammable materials usually found in a care setting. Prepare questions to ask on health and safety matters. (Core skills Communication 1.1.)

You have now studied the main four causes of fire in care establishments, but of course all of these also provide food for the client and cooking can also lead to fire hazard. Most important of these is a chip pan left unattended, perhaps the telephone rings or someone calls, the pan gets too hot and the oil sets on fire. Clients in their own homes can be particularly liable to these types of accidents. If you suspect a client may be unsafe cooking on their own, discuss this with your supervisor.

Safety equipment and systems for fire emergencies

- Fire doors should have signs on them and not be obstructed in any way or wedged open. Any fault with fire doors should be reported to the supervisor immediately.
- Exit doors should have clear signs and be well lit. Furniture and equipment should not be left in halls, stairways or passages. Outside paths should be kept free of snow and ice.
- Air vents on appliances and any heat sources like lamps should not be draped or covered with cloth, paper or plastic materials.
- Waste should be properly disposed of in the correct containers and not left near sources of heat.
- Make sure you know the procedure in case of fire in any establishment where you work or learn.

Student activity 3

- Think about fire safety in your own home and discuss with people who live around you what to do in the event of fire . Fire practice, fire lectures and training must be attended and the information learned. Other people's lives may depend upon you knowing what to do.
- Know the plan of your building and find out where fire alarms, fire extinguishers and exits are located. Find out the procedure for keeping clients safe. Never use lifts in any building if fire breaks out. If you are the first person to notice a fire – stay calm, remember what you have learned and sound the alarm. Report the fire in the correct way – this may mean telephoning the fire brigade direct (dial 999 and ask for the fire service) or the switchboard or a special person.

Student activity 4

- Write down the information you should give the person to whom you are reporting the fire and practise making such a 'phone call (not a real call of course, this wastes services and may cost lives). Find out the procedures in your school or college – not just for students, but staff as well.

Clients in the immediate fire area must be removed to a safer location. Get help as quickly as possible and use common sense in moving clients e.g. help a client to walk, or if on your own, roll a bed or use a blanket drag for a bedridden person.

Student activity 5

- Either ask trained staff in your workplace to show you and allow you to practise or practise on one another in school or college. Do not practise on clients!

Blanket drag – place a blanket folded lengthways on the floor beside the bed. Pull the 'client' to the edge of the bed using one arm under the neck and shoulders and the other arm under the knees. Drop down on to one knee the other at right angles and carefully lower the client so that your arms and knee are supporting them. Slide the client gently to the floor, make sure that they are centrally on the blanket and pull from the room head first on the blanket.

Two other carries you may want to practise are the two- or four-handed carry and the fore and aft carry (see first aid books, e.g. St. John/Red Cross First Aid Manual, 6th edition, Dorling Kindersley, 1992).

FIRE EXTINGUISHERS

Colour	Contents	Used for fighting ...
Red	Water	Burning wood, paper, cloth etc
Black	Carbon dioxide	Ignited liquids, gases, electrical equipment
Cream	Foam	Ignited liquids
Blue	Dry powder	Burning wood, paper, cloth, liquids, gases, electrical
Green	Halon	Ignited liquids, gases. electrical equipment

ALWAYS AIM AT THE BASE OF THE FIRE
Read the instructions often so that you know how they work before a fire starts
Fire extinguishers should be checked regularly.

All doors and windows should be closed to isolate an area and prevent a fire from spreading. Finally, be ready to follow instructions from trained people who are in charge.

Fire fighting

Only tackle a fire yourself if it is small and you are trained. There are many types of fire extinguishers and they are used for different types of fire. You will find the most common types listed in the table above.

Alternative ways of fighting fires, particularly in clients' homes, would be using water from buckets or hoses, smothering the flames with sand or cloths (wet folded tea towels are good for burning pans) such as blankets or beating with shovels.

 Key points with fire hazards are

- know how fires are caused
- practise preventive procedures
- report anything you feel is unsafe
- learn what to do in case of fire.

Student activity 6

 • Find out what is the main law relating to fire safety and who is responsible for notices and training.

Substances

In 1988, a set of regulations commonly called COSHH came into being. COSHH stands for the 'control of substances hazardous to health' and there was a period of time given so that people could alter their procedures to comply with the regulations. Every day people caring for others come into contact with a large number of substances which could have harmful effects on a person either in the place on the body where contact has been (called local effects) or affecting one or more systems of the body (called systemic effects). These harmful substances are said to be toxic or poisonous and this can occur soon after the contact or some considerable time afterwards. It can therefore be quite difficult to link the effect of the substance with a complaint suffered by the worker.

The types of illness commonly caused by toxic substances include skin irritations, asthma, headaches, feeling sick, vomiting, tiredness and not being able to sleep. There are many more. As you can see they are the sorts of conditions we all suffer from periodically and few think about associating them with substances we may have used one day at work or even everyday. Many of these substances are familiar everyday chemicals we use all the time like disinfectants, bleaches, detergents, sterilising agents, antibiotics and even mercury from broken thermometers.

Safety equipment and systems for reducing risk

All toxic substances should be clearly labelled with the chemical name (often different to the name given by the manufacturer), the hazards associated with the substance, the problems it can cause and the way it should be stored. You should be provided with this information and it is your employer's responsibility to make sure this happens. If you do not get this information, you have the right to ask for it.

If a less harmful substance will do the job just as well, the toxic substance should be replaced by this. You should also be provided with protective clothing to do the job.

Student activity 7

• Make a list of all the articles of protective clothing you can think of. Start with the head, eyes, nose, mouth etc. and work down until you reach the feet.

Cover all breaks in the skin with suitable dressings, and wash and dry hands carefully after using chemicals. Make sure you have had training in the use of toxic substances and that you follow all advice given.

Report any skin irritation or any other complaints that you think may have been the result of being in contact with toxic substances so that investigations may take place and any extra protection used.

Clean up any spilled materials at once and dispose of them in the correct manner. Ask someone if you are unsure what to do. Chemicals splashed onto clothing means that the clothing should be removed immediately before the liquid soaks through to the skin and any substances on the skin or in the eyes should be washed off with plenty of water. Medical advice should be sought. Signs and treatment of poisoning can be found in Elements 5.2 and 5.3.

Unsafe equipment

In the same way that care workers are using substances which may be hazardous, they are also in contact with equipment which might be badly chosen, poorly manufactured or not maintained properly. Equipment will include simple things like chairs and tables or complicated machines like those which take X-ray pictures and ECG traces of the heart's rhythm. You may be asked your opinion of the design of a piece of equipment because you are using it everyday. Do not be afraid to state why you think improvements are desirable.

Daily use should mean that you always check the equipment before use and report any faults which you find to a supervisor. If the fault is serious, take the equipment out of use, label it as faulty and await the result of your report. The item should then be investigated, modified, repaired or removed from use permanently. In large establishments, there will probably be special forms to complete for faulty equipment.

Most items for use will have instructions from the manufacturer clearly displayed for you to read. Money for buying replacement equipment is often in short supply, but this should not mean that anyone has to do their job with unsafe equipment.

A lot of accidents still occur in care establishments, involving 'sharps' which are not properly used or are disposed of incorrectly. 'Sharps' are syringe (hypodermic) needles, scalpels (very sharp hospital knives), broken glass ampoules (small sealed drug containers) and similar cutting items. Many workers who support main carers like doctors and nurses have been injured by sharps because the people who used them did not dispose of them correctly. They usually pick them up in ordinary rubbish and of course they cut through and injure the person who may be a porter, cleaner or support worker. As well as a painful and unpleasant injury, there is the risk of developing a serious disease such as hepatitis or HIV infection. Such conditions are life threatening and must be reported straight away, however slight the injury.

Unsafe environment

First, you might consider falls and trips; thousands of people are injured every year in falls in their workplace and over 100 die. You might think that most of these occur from high places, but most are actually at floor level.

 You should keep a watchful eye for hazards in walkways and passages.

The following is where or when most of these occur

- smooth, slippery floors
- stepping from baths, showers
- wet floors – cleaning, spills
- greasy floors – oil, grease
- snow and ice
- hidden steps – corners, entrances
- loose flooring – tiles, bricks, floorboards, paving slabs
- frayed carpets or loose rugs.

Trips usually occur from

- trailing electric flexes or telephone wires
- handbags, carrier bags, briefcases, sports-bags left on the floor
- drawers left open, particularly bottom drawers
- furniture which obstructs passageways
- fallen items, particularly toys, stored packages or piles of paper left on stairs, floors or in corridors.

Good housekeeping and careful observation can make sure many falls do not happen. Where young children and older people live together in the same house it is particularly important to watch for toys, especially wheeled ones left on stairs and walkways. Stairs should have secure hand rails. Statistics show us that falls are more dangerous for older people. Give an older person more time to move from place to place, more time to change direction and more time to climb and descend stairs.

Electrical sockets should be guarded so that little fingers or pointed things cannot be pushed into them. Baths and showers should be run and tested before children, clients with learning difficulties and older people are allowed into the water. Hand rails are useful close to the toilet and the bath for frail or disabled people. Many tragedies have happened in bathrooms and toilets because adaptations were not made or the activities there were unsupervised. Young children should not be allowed unsupervised access to water in ponds, rivers, baths etc. A small child can drown in only a few inches of water so keep a special watch on them.

Accidents frequently happen with kettles, cooking pans and other sources of heat. Guard rails should be placed on cookers, pan handles turned inwards and kettles well designed with flexes well out of reach. Over 1,000 accidents involving scalds to young children occur in the UK every year associated with kettles.

Lighting is always important, but particularly so for older people whose eyesight is not often good. Always make sure dead light bulbs are replaced at once and the electrical supply is switched off before doing so. When tackling something high like a ceiling light bulb, use a properly balanced step stool or step ladder to climb on. Never tilt a chair on two legs only and do not allow clients to do so, it is only too easy to fall backwards and suffer serious back injury as a result.

Care workers mainly wear some type of uniform at work, dress should be sensible without loose bits that catch on door handles or machinery. The use of trousers for females involved in lifting clients is becoming more acceptable and allows for better control of leg movements. Lifting is dealt with in Element 5.3, and the same principles should be used if carrying heavy loads.

Student activity 8

• Make a plan, diagram or sketch of one or two rooms in a home or care establishment and point out all the potential hazards for a particular client group.
• Complete you work by providing suggestions how you can make the environment safer.
• Share out the different types of rooms and client groups within your learning group and each make a presentation of your chosen environment and client group to the others.
• When listening to other people's presentations ask questions and make notes so that you have all covered the range of unsafe environments. (Core skills – Communication 1.1 and 1.3.)

Infectious diseases

Infectious diseases are diseases which spread from one person to another (or from an animal or insect). They are caused by very small creatures which can often only be seen through a special piece of equipment known as a microscope. For this reason, they are often called microorganisms, microbes or by usually unqualified people, germs. Microbes commonly met in care settings are either bacteria or viruses. Both are very simple forms of life, viruses being much smaller and simpler than bacteria. Most viruses are too small even to be seen by the types of microscopes found in schools and colleges.

Student activity 9

• Using your library, find three examples of a disease caused by bacteria and three by viruses. Try to find pictures of a virus and a bacterium to look at.

Viral diseases tend to have very short incubation periods, and short bouts of illness which come on quickly – there are several exceptions to this. Bacterial diseases are likely to have longer incubation periods and periods of illness starting more slowly and building up.

When people cannot see microbes they tend to forget their existence, so it is very important to protect yourself and your clients with cleanliness and good hygiene at all times. Everyone has microbes on their skin and in their bowels, these microbes are usually harmless and in fact give us some benefits. However, if these microbes get into other parts of our bodies they can be extremely harmful. We call harmful microbes, pathogens.

Care workers in all settings are constantly dealing with clients who have been vomiting, coughing, sneezing, or soiling themselves, clothes, bedlinen, toilets and bedpans. Care workers are in constant contact with infected material.

It is important to understand that microbes can enter bodies in several ways – by breathing in, from taking infected food, through any procedure where the skin is broken or cut (syringe needles, operations, injury etc.) or special procedures where tubes may be pushed into the body e.g. catheters to allow urine to escape from a blocked bladder. Infection can even enter the body through sexual intercourse.

Care establishments are potential breeding grounds for microbes, they lurk in bed clothes, flower vases, sinks, toilets, bedpan washers, creams, ointments etc. Care clients are more prone to infection because of age, illness, lowered resistance from drugs etc.

SAFETY PRECAUTIONS AND SAFE WORKING PRACTICES

So how best to protect yourself and your clients from passing on infection?

1 Probably the most powerful way of protecting everyone involved is simple hand washing – after using the toilet oneself, after changing or handling bedlinen, after dealing with any part of a client or their body products, and before eating a meal or handling food for clients. Dry tablets of soap, paper towels or hot-air hand dryers and wash basins should be plentiful and regularly cleaned.

2 Bagging of bedlinen by the bed, with special bags for soiled linen or infected linen to protect laundry workers.

3 Thorough cleaning using vacuum cleaners with air filters, cotton or nylon mops washed daily in hot water and stored dry, and colour-coded cloths for different areas. Spillages should be cleaned up immediately and if infected, material disinfected.

4 Flower vases changed regularly and vases washed and dried before reusing.

5 If disinfectants are used down toilets (usually flushing is more effective) the correct strength should be used.

6 Correct disposal of waste. Dressings and disposable items should be burned (incinerated).

7 Report any pest infestation.

8 Good food hygiene – involves correct storage of food, separating preparation

areas and kitchen equipment used for cooked and uncooked food, heating food thoroughly at a sufficiently high temperature, not allowing food to stand at room temperature for more than a few minutes. Good personal hygiene for catering staff should mirror that of the care workers.

9   All outbreaks of illness from infection should be reported and investigated to find the source of infection and to take further action to prevent it happening again.

10 For some procedures, protective clothing should be worn – but it should be disposed of the minute the procedure is carried out.

11 Regular training in fighting infection should be carried out.

12 Regular checks on procedures should be made. Human beings like to take short cuts.

Student activity 10

• Ask your catering manager of your school or college to talk to your group about the procedures in practice for preventing outbreaks of food poisoning, and about the training for catering staff.

• Construct a short report on the talk for your portfolio.

• If you are on work placement in a care establishment find out what infection control policies are in operation or invite a supervisor in to talk to your group about the procedures.

HEALTH AND SAFETY REGULATIONS

The main law controlling health and safety is the Health and Safety at Work Act passed in 1974.

 The key points from this act are as follows.

• Employers must protect the health, safety and welfare of the people who work for them. The act states that this is 'as far as is reasonably practicable'.

• If a person continuously takes no notice of the systems the employer tries to put into place, then the employer cannot be blamed if anything happens to the employee. Also, if something happens totally 'out of the blue' and nobody could have expected that to happen, the employer is not at fault.

• Your employer has a duty to make sure that while at work you are reasonably safe. If you are injured at work while employed you may be able to take your employer to court for payment for your injuries.

• The list below states the main duties of an employer towards the welfare and thus the safety of their work force by following procedures to

1   keep the floors clean
2   maintain floors and passageways
3   prevent overcrowding
4   keep the room temperature above 16 °C
5   make sure there is good ventilation (fresh air) and lighting
6   provide suitable toilets and places to wash with soap, hot and cold water and something to dry hands with

7 provide drinking water and somewhere to eat meals

8 employ people who are trained and competent to do the job

9 provide the right equipment, protective clothing and materials for the job

10 check that you take reasonable care with equipment

11 guard all dangerous machinery

12 provide first aid kits and someone trained in first aid

13 provide fire fighting equipment and training for fire hazards.

However, it is not only the employer who had duties, everyone also has to

- take reasonable care of their own health and safety
- take reasonable care for the safety of your fellow workers
- co-operate with the employer in health and safety matters
- not interfere with equipment provided for health and safety.

Health and Safety Executive personnel have powers to take people to court, close places down or ask for them to be improved within a set time period. People who break health and safety laws can be sent to prison or fined.

Student activity 11

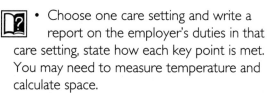

- Choose one care setting and write a report on the employer's duties in that care setting, state how each key point is met. You may need to measure temperature and calculate space.
- Try to find the safety policy of a care establishment – this is a written statement of the safety rules and regulations and how they are carried out e.g. a local hospital may ring the fire alarm bells every week at the same

time, to check that they are working properly. Hazards should be identified and procedures in place for monitoring, officers should be named and staff informed of dangers and precautions to be taken.

Many establishments also have a code of practice. The Government has been responsible for the introduction of various charters. These documents all state the standards of the organisation, what people can reasonably expect from the service, especially with responding time, and where they can complain.

Student activity 12

- Collect three copies of different charters and write a report comparing the detail in each one. Do people know the charters exist? Do they read them? Have they ever used them? You could survey this!

BENEFITS GAINED FROM FOLLOWING HEALTH AND SAFETY REGULATIONS

- Less accidents because more are prevented, this means less people dying, less people permanently or temporarily disabled or sick. All this means greater financial independence for the individual, less money paid out in welfare, benefits and medical treatment.
- Improved working conditions – people have better, cleaner, tidier places to work in. Hygienic washing and toilet places are provided, everyone has more space to work in and should be neither too hot nor too cold.
- Conditions are better too for clients, confidence and work enjoyment is high. Diseases are less likely to be encouraged if

cleanliness is important so stays in care may be shorter, staff absenteeism lower. This will give improved service all round.

Self-check questions

 1 Where do bacteria live naturally in the body?

2 What are the duties of an employee under the Health and Safety at Work Act (1974)?

3 What are the four main causes of fire in care establishments?

4 Give three common substances in daily use which might cause hazards to workers.

5 What material is found inside a red fire extinguisher and when is it used for fire fighting?

6 What are 'sharps' and why are they dangerous?

7 List three common causes of trips.

8 Which is the most important procedure in preventing infection passing from one person to another?

ELEMENT 5.2

Explore common health emergencies

At the end of this element you should have

- identified the common health emergencies which happen in care settings
- described the most important signs to observe in such emergencies
- described how you would care for someone suffering from a common health emergency
- identified which common health emergencies need the emergency services.

ELEMENT 5.3

Investigate emergency care procedures

At the end of this element you should be able to

- identify and describe appropriate care procedures in health emergencies
- describe how to monitor the patients' condition in health emergencies
- identify and describe how you would keep the patient and yourself free from injury and infection – safety procedures
- describe the correct procedures to use in accidents and emergencies.

These two elements are closely linked so they will be dealt with together as each emergency is studied.

The common health emergencies you need to learn about are

- asthma
- epileptic fit
- concussion
- burns
- scalds

- cuts
- electric shock
- choking
- broken bones
- heart attack
- poisoning.

As each of these emergencies is described, the care settings in which these are most likely to occur will be mentioned, followed by the key signs and the care procedures, or what you should do. Monitoring and safety procedures will come next as they are relevant to each emergency.

ASTHMA

This is a condition which causes difficulty in breathing, particularly in breathing out. Many adults have asthma, but it occurs more often in children and young people. It can occur in any care setting.

Key signs

- Difficulty in breathing – often wheezing.
- The sufferer will often be anxious or upset.
- There may be blueness of the lips and skin generally.
- If a severe attack is present, the asthma does not respond to treatment or occurs for a long time – then call the ambulance or doctor.

What to do

 1 Keep calm and reassure the person.

2 Sit the person forward at a table or similar surface with plenty of fresh air.

3 Help the person to take medication if this is with them.

4 Watch for signs that it is not getting better.

Most asthma attacks are triggered off by worry or the presence of some substance to which the person is sensitive (allergic). Many people are sensitive to animal hair, dust or pollen. However, asthma sufferers tend to have more attacks if the atmosphere is smoky or they have a respiratory infection. People who often have asthma attacks usually carry inhalers, this is like an aerosol (spray) which puffs out a certain amount of a special drug into their mouths and down into their lungs to help them breathe more easily.

You should monitor a person who is having an asthma attack by taking the pulse and breathing rate about every 10 minutes.

Taking the pulse

This represents the heart beat and can be felt where an artery is close to the surface of the body. The most common place to feel for an artery is at the wrist, below the base of the thumb. In babies, the wrists are very tiny so it is easier to take the pulse of a larger blood vessel on the inside of the upper arm. However, in an emergency or life threatening situation, these pulses may be hard to find because the blood is being pumped around the body slower and the pulse is becoming weaker, so the pulse at the neck is more useful. This is found between the windpipe of the neck and the muscle which runs from the ear to the lowest part of the neck in the middle. All these pulses can be found on both sides of the body.

Figure 35   *Neck and wrist pulse points*

waving your arms about or something similar and repeat the counting. What has happened to the pulse rate? This can also happen with raised body temperature, anaemia and loss of blood. Other conditions can do the opposite.
- If you can, try taking a child's or baby's pulse. This is much more difficult and may take a few attempts to count accurately. A minute seems a long time to count a pulse for, and can be tiring if you are doing it for some time. An easier way is to count for fifteen or thirty seconds and multiply by either four or two, to get the pulse rate in sixty seconds or one minute. Try this now.
- Find out what is the usual normal range of pulse rate for an adult, a child of about eight years of age and a young baby.

To find someone's breathing or respiratory rate, watch the rise and fall of a person's chest and count. The rib cage will move up and out and return to its first position. This is one breath. It can be difficult when a person is clothed, you can also watch for the 'tummy' moving in and out or the sounds of breathing. Breathing rate is much slower than pulse rate but it too increases with infections, fever and exercise.

Student activity 13

- Find a partner and practise counting and recording the number of beats or pulses occurring in one minute, using your fingers lightly placed on the pulse. Do not use your thumb as it has a pulse of its own and you could be counting your own pulse instead of your partner's! Try to get used to the rhythm and strength of the beats after you have counted them. How will you record pulse beats if you are monitoring someone's pulse?
- Carry out a little physical exercise, such as running up and down steps a few times,

Student activity 14

- Why not repeat activity 13, but this time as well as counting pulse, count breaths as well, at rest and doing moderate and hard physical exercise. You can collect all the figures together – called data – and make a table to present your results. You could calculate the mean using the formula below.

$$\text{Mean} = \frac{\text{all the numbers for the same thing added together}}{\text{the number of numbers for that thing}}$$

For example, a class group found that their resting pulse rates were 69, 76, 67, 70, 72, 65, 72, 69 beats every minute. When these are added together they make 560, but there are 8 numbers in the row, so the mean is 560 ÷ 8, this is 70 beats per minute. You could calculate mean pulses and breathing rates at rest and after exercise. (Application of Number 1.3.)

EPILEPTIC FIT

There are a few types of fit. In babies and young children, a fit is common when the body temperature is raised well above normal. This is known as a fever and the type of fit is often called a febrile (which means feverish) convulsion. You may come across this in any care setting involving babies and young children.

Key signs

- Hot, pink skin and sometimes sweating.
- Muscle twitchings, arched back, clenched fists.
- Breath holding, redness or even blueness of face.
- Drooling at the mouth.

What to do

1 Make sure the child cannot injure itself – you can put padding or pillows around.
2 Remove clothes and bedclothes to cool the child.
3 Sponge with very slightly warm (tepid) water, starting at the head and working down.

4 If necessary, place the child in the recovery position to keep the airway open.
5 Reassure others who may be frightened that the fit is rarely dangerous, but the high temperature has to be looked at by qualified medical help. Often this will mean calling an ambulance, but if at home, the child's own doctor may be called more quickly.

Major fits or grand mal fits will often occur quickly, sometimes with a warning sign, such as odd behaviour, strange smell or taste and sometimes without warning at all. Anyone can have a fit, but people who have brain damage or head injuries are more likely to have regular fits. This means clients in residential establishments, nurseries and hospitals are more likely to have fits.

Key signs

- The individual suddenly becomes unconscious and falls.
- The back is arched and the muscles stiff.
- Breathing usually stops and this causes a blueness around the face and neck.
- Muscles start to contract and twitch, breathing becomes noisy.
- The individual may pass urine or open their bowels during the fit.
- The muscles relax and breathing starts again within a few minutes.
- The person recovers consciousness and may sleep for a while or appear dazed.

What to do

1 Make sure the client has space around and try to protect from injury by easing the fall or pillowing the head.

2 Leave the client unrestrained, leave the mouth alone and let the client remain where they are unless in a very dangerous place.
3 Loosen clothing around the neck.
4 Stay with the person and place in the recovery position when breathing starts again.
5 If the fit lasts for more than a few minutes call an ambulance.
6 If the fit is the first or it is followed by more fits, call the ambulance or doctor.

CONCUSSION

This is when the brain inside the skull has been shaken by a blow of some sort to the head. If you have ever made a jelly or a blancmange in a mould and shaken it to release it, it often has tiny tears in the outside. This is similar to what can happen to the brain after a blow. A blow to the head can happen in any place and therefore in any care setting. Older people and adventurous children often fall and are particularly likely to become concussed.

Key signs

- Brief loss of consciousness.
- Mild headache.
- Feeling of dizziness or feeling sick on recovery.
- Loss of memory of what happened.

What to do

1 Watch closely for any worsening of condition after recovery.
2 Do not allow the person to just carry on. The person should always see a doctor,

this usually means being taken to hospital. In some cases you might have to call an ambulance, but the person could be taken by car.
3 However, if the person does not become conscious quickly, say after three minutes, place in the recovery position and call an ambulance.

In several care procedures now, you have been told to put the individual in the recovery position.

RECOVERY POSITION

This is the position for an unconscious or dazed person who is breathing and has a pulse.

Kneel beside the person who should be lying on the back with legs straight. Tilt the head back and lift the chin to allow air to get to the lungs. Place the arm nearest to you out and bend up at the elbow, with the palm of the hand facing you.

Now, bring the other arm across the person's chest, holding the hand against their cheek with the palm outwards again. Notice both palms face outwards. With your other hand, pull up the knee of the far leg keeping their foot on the ground.

With your two hands in this position, carefully and gently pull the person towards you until they are resting on their hand underneath the head and the upper leg, the one you pulled is supporting the body bent at the knee.

Adjust the position of the head so that it is still tilted back and make sure the person is in a secure position.

Monitor pulse and breathing regularly, keeping records if you can.

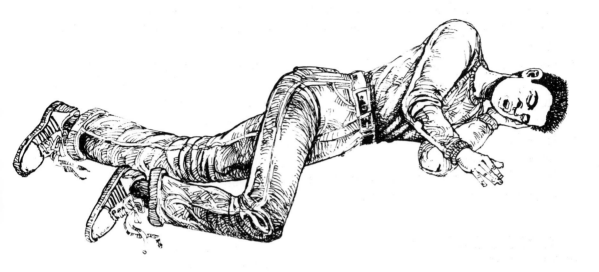

Figure 36   *The recovery position*

BURNS AND SCALDS

A burn is caused when dry heat damages the body, like touching a hot pan on the cooker and a scald is an injury from wet heat, like steam from a kettle.

These injuries can occur in any setting, but are more common with toddlers and young children, who often do not realise the dangers, and older people who may be forgetful or are slow and unsteady in their movements.

Burns can be shallow, only affecting the outer layer of skin; these are minor burns if they only affect a small area. They can be deeper, causing blisters to form and showing the same signs as above, or very deep, damaging all layers of the skin and even parts underneath.

Key signs

- Redness.
- Pain.

- Swelling – these are the shallow burns.
- Blisters with surrounding raw skin – these are deeper burns.
- Pale, waxy often scorched skin – these are very deep burns.

Special points to note about burns and scalds

Burns and scalds can cause shock because they destroy the body's waterproof skin layer, letting body fluid leak out – this is shown by the blisters. If a large area is involved, shock is greater and the person's life is in danger.

This type of injury also destroys the skin's natural ability to defend the body against microbes and infection.

Body cells will go on burning for a time after the person gets away from the heat unless the area of skin is cooled down.

What to do

 1 With a very deep burn, send for medical help immediately.
2 With an extensive burn, send for medical help as well — see below about deciding on this.
3 Cool the area with lots of cold water. Do this for at least 10 minutes. If a limb is affected, immerse all the burned area in a sink or bath; if part of the chest or trunk then pour on water with the person lying down.
4 Check breathing and circulation while you are doing this, resuscitate if necessary.
5 Carefully remove or loosen any tight jewellery or clothing before the area swells up.
6 Cover the burned area with a sterile dressing, clean cloth or clingfilm to prevent infection. Plastic bags are useful for hands and feet.

What not to do

 1 Never remove anything which is sticking to the burn.
2 Never handle the damaged area.
3 Never apply any 'remedies' to the burn e.g. witchhazel, butter, ointment etc.
4 Never burst blisters.
5 Never use fluffy coverings.
6 Never attach dressings to damaged skin.

If you can, estimate how much skin is involved if the burn is shallow or the deeper (blistered) type. Do not spend much time on this – if you cannot do it, and it is more than the area you can cover with your hand, get medical help.

The area of the body's surface can be divided into percentage areas of 9%. The diagram in Figure 37 shows you how.

If a hand area is involved, then get medical help. If a '9% area' is involved, the person should be taken to hospital as shock is likely to occur. If the person has a very deep burn – hospital without delay e.g. by ambulance or car. If in doubt, get to hospital as soon as possible.

Children and babies can have a large area of their skin burned or scalded by a relatively small accident because they are so small. Only treat very minor small burns yourself.

Remember, burns can have many causes which can be dangerous to you such as fires, electricity, chemicals etc. Always check your

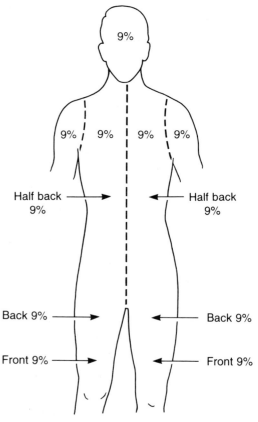

Figure 37   *Percentage areas of the body*

own safety in such events – do not make more victims! Any burn involving the air passages, including the mouth may cause the patient to suffocate and needs special treatment in hospital without delay.

Cuts

Cuts or wounds can happen anywhere to any person. They may be cuts from a blade or sharp edge which bleed a lot but heal well, or tears of the skin which bleed less, take a longer time to heal and are likely to become infected.

Key signs

- Bleeding.
- Pain.
- Break in the skin surface.

What to do

1 Wash your hands quickly but thoroughly in hot soapy water before and after dealing with the cut.
2 Stop bleeding by raising the part (or lowering the rest of the body) and apply direct pressure to the wound edges. Safety point – you should protect yourself against contact with body fluids of another person if you possibly can. Wear disposable gloves or put your hands inside clean plastic bags, cover any sores or breaks in your own skin with dressings, apply the pressure over a dressing or clean cloth. You will also be protecting the victim from any infection you may be carrying as well.
3 Put on a sterile dressing or clean cloth over any other material you may have

used. If the blood comes through, put another dressing on top of the old one.
4 Check for any other injuries.
5 If the cut is deep or long, dirty, fails to stop bleeding, or you suspect other injuries, get medical help as soon as possible.
6 Be aware that shock can develop quickly if much blood is lost and send the client to hospital without waiting.
7 Watch the patient carefully for signs of lowered consciousness – confusion, not answering questions, groaning, flickering of eyelids etc. – place in recovery position after stopping bleeding, monitor pulse, breathing and patient's responses to you.
8 Treat for shock if help was delayed and bleeding was considerable, by raising legs, lowering head and covering patient with a blanket.

Electric shock

When a person comes into contact with electricity we say they get an electric shock. This can happen in any care setting which has unsafe or faulty electrical equipment, flexes to appliances which have become frayed or unguarded or overloaded electrical connection points. Children are particularly at risk, as in most homes electric sockets are near the ground and they are likely to poke things into any unguarded holes. Older people may not check their electrical equipment very often and forget about safe procedures, so once again this is a hazard for everybody to guard against, but care settings for the young and the old especially.

Key signs

 • Victim will be badly shaken or even unconscious.
- Breathing and heart action may stop.
- Electrical burns (often deep burns) where the current has entered and left the skin.
- Signs of shock – rapid pulse, cold clammy (damp) grey skin, feeling sick and thirsty.

It is important to note that if you touch the casualty with bare hands while the current is still flowing through the victim, you will also experience electric shock. If the area is wet, the chances of electric shock are greater. This is why there are no electric points in bathrooms, only pull switches. Remember, electricity and water are very dangerous together.

What to do

 1 Switch off the current at the quickest point.
2 Then, and only then, check breathing and pulses, resuscitating if necessary.
3 Cool any burns (see procedure under burns).
4 Place in the recovery position and send for emergency medical services.
5 If apparently unharmed, rest and call the doctor to check over.

If for any reason you cannot switch off the current, you can try to knock the victim away from the source of electricity using a broomhandle, chair or similar *wooden* material. Never use anything metal which will conduct the electricity through you. Make sure you are standing on raised wood, plastic rubber or thick paper to insulate your body from the source. Only do this as a last resort, it is very dangerous for you.

CHOKING

This occurs when an object gets stuck at the back of the throat and blocks the air passages. Objects are usually food, sweets and small toys. Obviously, care settings for young children are particularly likely, but choking is fairly common in older people who may not chew their food properly and have weaker muscles.

Key signs

 • Victim suddenly grasps throat or coughs violently.
- Voice affected – may have difficulty in speaking.
- Breathing becomes gasping and troublesome.
- Skin colour, particularly lips, may look blue.

What to do

 1 Bend the victim until the head is lower than the chest.
2 Give several hard slaps with a flat hand between the shoulder blades, use less force for a child and even less for a baby.
3 If this fails to remove the blockage, and the victim is an adult or older child try the abdominal thrust. Standing behind the victim, lock your hands together under the rib cage at the front and pull sharply inwards and upwards against the chest. Your hands should have the fingers locked into one another, one hand palm up and the other palm down. Try this four or five times and if it does not unblock the air passages repeat back slaps and thrusts alternately about five times each.

4 If the victim becomes unconscious begin resuscitation and send for the emergency medical services.

Several people have died because they started to choke and ran to the bathroom, often people laughed at them. Follow someone who is choking and help in the way described above. It is not a laughing matter and can be a serious medical emergency.

Do not give abdominal thrusts to a baby, and only perform this on a child if you are sure you know what to do, otherwise begin resuscitation.

POISONING

Poisons are substances which damage the body, they may be taken accidentally or deliberately to end life. Many poisons are ordinary household substances used for cleaning, disinfecting or use in the garden. Children are most likely to be affected by accidental poisoning. Deliberate poisoning is likely to involve misusing medicines or drugs, alcohol or glues, and is more likely in adolescents and adults.

Key signs

- Some poisons may be present around the person or there may be a smell in the area.
- The person may be unconscious, not breathing and without pulses.
- If conscious, the person may show unusual behaviour – this can be inactivity and sleepiness or wild, excitable behaviour.
- Pulses may be unusually fast or abnormally slow and weak.
- Complaints of feeling sick or actual vomiting may occur.

- Pupils, the central black part of the eyes, may be very small or unusually large.

From your reading so far you can see there are several different pictures you might get of poisoning. Different poisons produce different effects.

A witness might be able to describe what happened to the victim, particularly if this happened at work or socially. You must always be careful not to contaminate yourself with any poison, particularly if you are called on to resuscitate the victim. Remember to keep any bottles, tablets or anything similar which might enable the emergency services to identify the poison that was taken.

What to do

1 Chemicals on the skin – wash away with plenty of water protecting yourself with gloves or something similar.
2 Chemicals which have been breathed in – remove the victim if possible into fresh air. Remember safety for yourself first.
3 In all cases, except the most trivial, watch for the need to commence resuscitation and call the emergency services. Place in the recovery position if unconscious but with breathing and with pulses. Keep checking at regular intervals.
4 Make sure you do not make the victim vomit, this may be very dangerous.

HEART ATTACK

This occurs when part of the muscle of the heart loses its blood supply. The effects depend on how much muscle is affected.

Adults over 40 years of age are the most likely group to have heart attacks. Although many older people have heart attacks they often do not show the classic signs shown by younger adults.

Key signs

* Study Figure 38 to remember the main signs of a heart attack.

What to do

1 Let the victim settle into the most comfortable position for them. This is often half sitting, half lying with support at their backs and under their knees.
2 If the victim is conscious, an aspirin chewed slowly will often ease the effects.

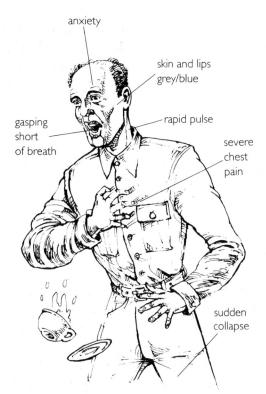

Figure 38   *Main signs of a heart attack*

3 Call the emergency services.
4 Monitor consciousness, breathing and pulses. Be ready to resuscitate if necessary.

BROKEN BONES

These are also called fractures. In children, fractures of bones may not be complete but cracks similar to that obtained if you bend a green branch of a bush or tree. Such breaks are 'greenstick' fractures, and occur because a child's bones are more bendable than adults'. Older people have more brittle or less solid bones than younger adults and their bones break more easily. Fractures, particularly of the arm and hip, are more common in care settings for older people, who are unsteady and more likely to fall.

Key signs

* Recent knock or fall.
* Pain at the site of injury.
* Swelling and often bruising.
* Deformity.
* There may be signs of shock, particularly if a major bone is broken.

What to do

1 Support and hold the injured part.

2 Tie to a rigid part of the body e.g. arm in sling to chest, damaged leg to good leg. Always tie from the joint above the injury to the joint below the injury to stop movement. Pad all bony lumps with soft padding e.g. between legs.
3 If the fracture is known as an open fracture, which means there is an open wound in the skin, any bleeding must

first be controlled by direct pressure over a pad (however, do not press on bone ends) – see section on cuts. Pad well with cotton wool and bandage. If bone ends are protruding build up the area with non fluffy material such as gauze pads before bandaging over the pads. Make the area unable to move as described before.

4 Send for the emergency service.

5 Make sure you do not bandage so tightly that blood flow is partly blocked or stopped. You can test this by pressing on a finger or toenail until it goes white, then releasing the pressure and checking to see if the pink colour returns. If it does not the bandage is too tight.

6 Keep the client still unless he/she is in danger, do not move them until the broken bone is fixed.

7 Prevent the client from eating or drinking in case he/she has to have an operation.

RESUSCITATION

When looking at the 'what to do' sections of several emergencies, there has been the need to resuscitate. Now, let us look at the ways in which you could do this. However, it cannot be emphasised often enough that you really cannot learn this on your own. **You need special equipment and a trained person to teach you** and then tell you if you are doing it incorrectly.

When a casualty is not breathing and is turning bluish-grey you must get some oxygen from your breath into their chest as soon as possible. Approximately 20% of the air around us is oxygen, when we have breathed this in and used some of the oxygen, there is still 16% left. Enough to support another person, so this is why mouth to mouth resuscitation works.

You cannot try this with another breathing person, so 'emergency' technology has provided us with dummies or, more correctly, manikins on which to practice. Manikins usually have the facility of inflatable chests and compressible hearts. They are quite expensive so you will have to join a first aid class if you do not have one available for your use.

With the casualty flat on their back, your first aim is to open the person's air passages. Put one hand under the person's neck and the other on their forehead, while gently tilting backwards until the nostrils point to the sky.

Taking care sweep your finger around the casualty's mouth to remove any obstruction.

Close the casualty's nose by pinching the nostrils with the thumb and forefinger.

Take a breath for yourself and seal your mouth around the casualty's mouth. As you blow gently but firmly into their mouth watch to see if the chest rises, take your mouth away to breathe for yourself and watch the chest fall. Repeat the process 10 times to load up their lungs with oxygen. Check that the pulse is still there. If you can, call or telephone for help between series of 10 breaths, checking the pulse at these intervals as well. If you are doing it properly, you should begin to see a change in colour, particularly in the lips and tongue.

If the colour does not improve check the way that you are doing it, especially opening the airway, and that the pulse is present. If the chest is failing to rise, check your airway position, your mouth seal, nose blocked off correctly and any obstruction is cleared. Continue until the casualty begins to breathe on their own (then place in recovery position

Figure 39   *Mouth to mouth resuscitation*

and check regularly), or expert help arrives. Your rate should be approximately 15 breaths each minute.

Young children and babies

Aged four and under, lie child along arm and seal mouth around child's mouth *and* nose give short, gentle breaths about 20/minute.

When there is no pulse

If the heart stops pumping blood around the body, you will have to be the pump until expert help arrives or the heart starts again. The oxygen needs to be carried to the body in general, and brain in particular. On the other hand, a person's heart may be pumping blood, but they may have stopped breathing, in which case, the heart will soon stop due to lack of oxygen.

In both these emergencies mouth to mouth resuscitation will need to be combined with chest compression and the two techniques together are known as cardio pulmonary resuscitation or CPR.

CHEST COMPRESSION

First, check the carotid pulse (not the wrist pulse) which is one of two large arteries lying on either side of the windpipe in the neck. Feel with two fingers pressed deep into the side of the neck (see Figure 35).

Student activity 15

- Take your own carotid pulse, by counting for fifteen seconds and multiplying it by four. Now take a friend's or a relative's carotid pulse to get practice in feeling for it.

If the carotid pulse is absent this means that the heart is not working and you must commence chest compression immediately.

External chest compressions, if correctly performed, will artificially pump about one-third of the body's blood around the circulation, and if this is oxygenated it will keep the casualty alive for the time being.

The method traps the heart between the vertebral column at the back and the rib cage/breastbone at the front and this expels blood from the heart towards the lungs and into the main artery (the aorta). As the pressure is released more blood is sucked into the heart from the big veins supplying it.

Student activity 16

- Ask your teacher to show you a skeleton and a heart model. Find the place where the heart should be inside the chest and carry out the measuring described below.

METHOD OF CHEST COMPRESSION

The pressure must be applied to the correct place for success. Feel for the notch at the base of the neck between the two collar bones and also for the notch where the ribs meet in the centre at the bottom of the rib cage. Find the halfway point between these two notches, then find the halfway mark of the lowest of these halves.

Kneeling beside the casualty at the level of your marked spot, place the heel of your hand on this point and the heel of your other hand on top interlocking the fingers together. The heel of your hand is the muscular bit above the wrist at the bottom of the palm.

Lean forwards over the casualty with straight arms and push firmly down until the chest is compressed at least four to five centimetres then releasing. Keep the actual fingers off the chest only using the heel of the lowest hand and do not move the hands in between compressions. You must aim for sixty to eighty pumps/minute (more for children and babies). Experts agree that to help you keep to time, it is useful to say one and two and three and four, up to fifteen, then begin again.

CPR

Before you start CPR (but do not delay for long – remember the brain cannot work without oxygen for more than three minutes) try to shout or 'phone for help. CPR is exhausting and if you are on your own you may not be able to continue for long.

ON YOUR OWN

Carry out two breaths then fifteen chest compressions followed by two breaths, fifteen compressions and so on. Do not stop to check pulses until you see some sign of blood circulation. If the heart begins again, check breathing – continue mouth to mouth if absent. If present, place in recovery position and check both every three minutes.

WITH ANOTHER HELPER

First helper goes for help while second begins CPR as above. When they return, one at head ventilating the lungs and one working on heart compression is the most usual. One breath is given after every five compressions of the chest. Monitor as above.

Exchange tasks every few minutes so that you can keep it up for longer. This time the 'breathing' person can check the pulse as well, every few minutes.

Remember, do not practise on a living person. Do join a class and get trained properly in the techniques.

Student activity 17

- Role play a selected number of health emergencies, describing what you are looking for and what you would do in those circumstances. Different groups could act out several different emergencies and the audience ask them questions. The role plays could be videoed for evidence.
- Alternatively, let each group investigate an emergency and present their findings to the rest of the group. They can then answer the audience's questions and evaluate the learning activity at the end.
- Students could write personal reports of other groups' presentations and include the notes and visual displays for their own evidence.

Self-check questions

1 In which care setting is accidental poisoning most likely to occur?
2 List the safety precautions you must take when asked to help a person who has had an electric shock?
3 What is the care procedure for a person who has had a heart attack?
4 How would you recognise a fracture?
5 What are the key signs for a major epileptic fit?
6 How would you help a peer suffering from an attack of asthma?
7 What is the difference between a burn and a scald?
8 Describe or demonstrate how you would place someone in the recovery position.
9 What medical emergency would you use the abdominal thrust for?
10 Describe the abdominal thrust?
11 Who should not have this care procedure?
12 List five key signs which might occur in poisoning?
13 What are the right materials to stand on when trying to release somebody from live electricity?
14 What causes infection?
15 What care procedures are designed to stop infection occurring in a burn.
16 Explain what you would do if someone at your placement had an epileptic fit?
17 A cut arm is bleeding badly. How would you treat the emergency?
18 In a care procedure, chewing an aspirin could be part of the treatment. What is the emergency?
19 Which group of people are most likely to have greenstick fractures?
20 What are the key signs of electric shock?

6

PLANNING DIETS

More and more research shows us how important the food we eat is in keeping us healthy. It is not only the type of food but also how much of each food we eat. Some people eat foods they have chosen specially, other people eat anything that is prepared for them and yet more people eat only a few types of food that is available. A healthy mix of foods in the right amounts to maintain health is known as a balanced diet, and in this chapter we will look at balanced diets, their advantages and disadvantages. In addition, we will explore the food needs of different people, what affects their choice of food and why they need to have special food. Finally, the planning and budgeting of diets for different individuals will be looked at.

ELEMENT 6.1

Exploring the main features of a healthy diet

At the end of this section you should have

- identified the main nutrients and provided examples
- identified the main food groups and provided examples
- described the function of the main food groups
- described the contents and character of a well-balanced diet
- described the benefits of a well-balanced diet
- described the disadvantages of a poor or unbalanced diet.

MAIN NUTRIENTS

What is food?

Food is any solid or liquid which when consumed gives us

- energy, enabling our bodies to function correctly and to move, and keeping our body temperatures inside normal limits
- raw materials to build new body cells or repair existing ones.

Food contains different quantities of nutrients which give us this energy and raw materials. The branch of science dealing with food and all the processes leading to growth, repair and maintaining the human body is called nutrition, and you will probably come across this word many times. Some nutrients are needed by the body in large amounts every day, these are called macronutrients. Micronutrients, on the other hand, are only needed in very tiny amounts daily.

What is a diet?

When people use this word in everyday conversation, we tend to think they are going to go on a weight reducing diet. This is probably because nearly all of us know someone 'on a diet' at some time – and they are trying to lose or sometimes gain weight. This explanation mirrors our society, it seems few people are happy with their body image.

Diet actually means food, menu or nourishment and has nothing at all to do with losing or gaining weight. A diet, then, is a mixture of food actually eaten in the course of one day and it usually includes the quantities we eat as well.

To understand quantities of food, you will need to understand the units of measurement of weight. Kilograms are very large units and you would be very unusual if you ate kilograms of food each day. Total body weight is now measured in kilograms, but many people in the UK tend to only know their weight in the old units of stones and pounds.

Figure 40   *Diet includes quantity not just quality*

Student activity 1

• Find your own weight in kilograms and grams. Ask some of your class, family or friends if they know their weight in old and new units and record their answers. This is called conducting a survey. You could add these numbers up and present your findings as a conclusion. Try to ask at least 20 people, more if you can, so you have some sensible results. If you wish to gain some work towards core skills (Application of Number 1.1) you could construct a table, graph or scale showing the relationship between old and new units. When people do not know their weight in new units, you could read the new unit from your conversion chart and tell them.

Food quantities need to be measured in smaller units called grams, usually shown by the letter 'g', smaller units milligrams, 'mg' or very small units micrograms μg. The difference between these units is 1,000 times every time.

1 kilogram is equal to 1,000 grams
1 gram is equal to 1,000 milligrams
1 milligram is equal to 1,000 micrograms

Student activity 2

• Work out how many milligrams are in 1.5 grams.
• Work out how many micrograms are in 0.5 grams.
• Calculate how many grams are in 12,300 milligrams.

Food groups and examples of each group

As well as water, which is required by every single living thing in order to survive, there are six food groups. Table 6.1.1 shows you the names of the food group and some examples of foods in each group.

Food group	Examples of foods in group
Macronutrients	
Carbohydrate	sugar, potatoes, bread, rice, pasta, maize, jam
Protein	egg, milk, fish, meat, beans, cereals, cheese
Fat	butter, margarine, egg yolk, cheese, oil, lard
Micronutrients	
Mineral salts	Iron – liver, kidney, red meat, egg yolk, beans, cereals Calcium – milk, cheese, bones (fish, ribs) Iodine – sea fish, shell fish, vegetables, salt
Vitamins	A – liver, cheese, butter, milk, eggs B – several cereals, peas, beans C – oranges, lemons, potatoes, blackcurrants D – butter, milk, cheese, liver
Fibre	wholemeal bread, bran, stalks of vegetables, potato skins

Table 6.1.1 *Food groups and examples*

Notice also on this table which foods are macronutrients and which micronutrients.

Student activity 3

• Find the labels of six foods which you regularly eat or drink. Draw a table (or spreadsheet if you can do this on a computer) to put in the name of the food, the types of foods it contains and whether they are macro or micronutrients. You can put in the quantities as well, as this might come in useful in another element.

Table 6.1.2 gives an idea to get you started but there are several ways of doing this, and you might prefer one of your own.

Fill in the rest of the table following the labels of your chosen food. You may need to ask some tutors or look up some names. Suggested foods to try: butter or margarine, corned beef, yoghurt, crisps, jam, bread, tinned fruit.

Food chosen/100g	Food group name	Quantity/100g	Macro or micro?
Bar of fruit and nut chocolate	protein carbohydrate fat	7.8g 56.0g 24.5g	macro macro macro
Butter or margarine			

Table 6.1.2   *Identifying food groups and nutrients in common foods.*

If you are going to compare different substances like food, you need to consider the same amount of each. For this reason most labels will tell you what 100g of the food contain. Use these figures. If a label gives only the information to be found in the food quantity on sale, you will have to find what 1g contains and then multiply by 100 to find what 100g contains – e.g. if a 52g chocolate bar had 4.1g of protein in it then 100g would have 5.2g ÷ 4.1g × 100. This works out at 7.8g as shown in the table.

Now you know what the food groups are and the types of foods you find in each group, it would be sensible to find out why we should eat these foods. If you study Figure 41 you will find out the important reasons why we eat these foods.

What is a balanced diet?

A balanced diet contains

• enough food to supply energy for body needs (carbohydrate and fat)
• enough food to repair and replace body cells (protein)
• vitamins and mineral salts in the correct proportions to develop and maintain the body in a healthy condition
• fibre to prevent constipation
• water to maintain the body.

So how should these foods be combined to make up a healthy well-balanced diet?

Many committees and organisations made up of nutrition experts have tried to put forward the idea of recommended daily intakes

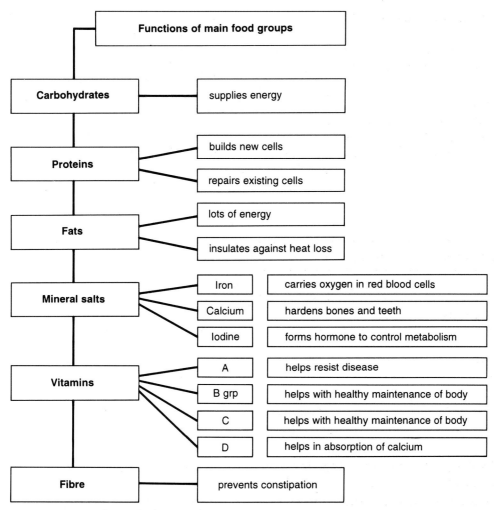

Figure 41   *Functions of main food groups*

of various nutrients. This is a very difficult thing to do as each individual is unique in their level of activity, their body shape and size, their state of health, age, place for living and its climate and many other factors. It means that when experts announce recommended daily intakes (RDIs) they have to include all healthy people and have based their figures on many groups of people living in many different places. What happens then, is that a recommended daily intake of, for example, protein is far greater than most

people need, or put another way, many people manage perfectly well on much less protein than the daily figure recommended by the experts. However, if an individual's protein intake keeps reducing and it started under the RDI, they are in danger of becoming medically ill over a period of time.

Not every nutrient has a stated RDI, as many will be met if the main RDIs are met.

As well as RDIs, food diets are usually quoted in energy terms. In other words, how much energy a particular combination of foods is likely to provide for an individual. This should match the energy used by that person and is therefore probably unique to that individual.

Energy requirements in kilojoules

Energy is measured in joules. One joule is quite a small unit when dealing with food, so we usually talk about 1,000 joules at a time and this is called a kilojoule (kJ, note small k but capital J).

The average adult male (but remember we said everyone was different) probably needs about 2,400kJ from daily food, just to support them through eight hours of sleep. A similar period, not doing very much (like watching television, reading a book or just chatting) but being awake, uses a few more kilojoules, about 3,000kJ. So you can imagine that being active at work, running for a bus, walking the dog etc., is going to need even more kilojoules and we can use around 7,000kJ doing these things. We have tried to divide the day up into three eight-hour periods but some people will sleep less and be active longer and vice versa. For any individual we can only estimate. If we add these periods up to make a 24-hour day we arrive at an energy need of 12,400kJ for the day.

It will be useful to take this as a baseline. If you research energy values of diets, you may come across another unit, the megajoule – this is 1,000 kilojoules, so our 'average diet' converted to megajoules would be 12,400 divided by 1,000 which equals 12.4MJ.

Would you think the average British woman, not pregnant or breastfeeding an infant, would take more or less than a male? If you said less, you would be correct, about 9–10MJ. Older people need less still as they are not very active compared to younger people. Pregnant and breastfeeding women take nearly but not quite as much as a male. Teenagers, usually fairly active, need nearly as much energy as an adult of the same gender. Children around three to four years of age need about half the adult requirement – they sleep a lot more, but are hardly ever still when they are awake! This is how you can estimate by using certain standards that you know.

Student activity 4

- See if you can estimate the energy requirements for the following categories.

1 75-year-old woman
2 8-year-old boy
3 very athletic 25-year-old man
4 33-year-old mother of two babies, one is still breastfed

If you managed to do these quite well, you have moved towards some Element 2 work.

It is obviously going to be useful for us to know the relationship between the main food groups and energy. This is quite easy: protein and carbohydrate when broken down by our body processes yield about 17kJ for every gram consumed. Fat, on the other hand, is much more energy concentrated and releases 37kJ for every gram processed. A fairly good rule of thumb when considering design of diets is 20% should be proteins, 20% fats and 60% carbohydrates. Vitamins, minerals and fibre weigh very little and do not produce energy so they can be discounted as substantial contributions to the diet – though of course they must be present.

Still using our 'standard' individuals, how much protein are they recommended to eat daily? Here in the UK, protein foods, although a little more expensive, are still readily available and most adult males consume about 70g per day. This actually is about 30g more than that required by the RDI but the diet is far more interesting as a result.

Examine your food group table with its quantities listed and see how many ways you can find of making up 70g of protein in a day. For example, there is about 12g of protein in one boiled egg, so to make up your protein requirements for a day you would have to eat around six eggs – for most people this would soon be very boring and they would not feel like eggs at all after a few days.

Clearly then, it is a good idea to include a wide variety of foods to maintain interest and appetite. Another way of considering how much protein the average person requires is 10% of the energy needs. So a diet providing 12,400kJ would need 1,240kJ supplied from protein, so divided by 17kJ this would indicate the number of grams of protein needed daily i.e. 73g.

RDIs are provided for iron and calcium because of the important links with blood and the carriage of oxygen and the hardness of the skeleton for support. About 500mg of calcium and 10mg of iron are required for the adult male, with the pregnant or breast-feeding mother needing more calcium and iron to supply the developing infant's needs as well, and children requiring more calcium than adults, to harden the skeleton and teeth.

Calcium and vitamin D tend to go hand in hand, but in sunlight humans can make vitamin D under their skin so reducing the need for it in the diet. Children may, however, need added vitamin D in the diet or as extras to the diet (cod liver oil for example).

All individuals need between 20mg and 30mg of vitamin C (apart from pregnant and breastfeeding women who need double that amount). An apple gives 5g but the same amount of blackcurrants give 200mg, while oranges supply 50mg. How many apples would you need to eat to supply your vitamin C requirement?

Two examples have shown us that we could supply our RDIs with only a few foods, but this would not provide the other nutrients a wide mixed diet would and we may become poorly nourished as a result. Two important UK committees are called COMA and NACNE, they have suggested the importance of

- eating more fresh, wholesome food and less processed food
- eating more foods from plants and less from animals
- eating less salt, sugar and fat in total
- drinking less tea, coffee, fizzy drinks and alcohol.

Student activity 5

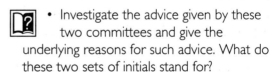

- Investigate the advice given by these two committees and give the underlying reasons for such advice. What do these two sets of initials stand for?
- Find out for yourself the RDI for vitamin A and add it to your notes.

Effects of balanced and unbalanced diets

After studying all this, you might naturally be thinking – 'what good does a balanced diet do. . . . and what will happen to me if I don't eat a balanced diet?'

On a balanced diet, you are far more likely to be the correct weight for your height and therefore not suffer from the effects of being overweight: extra wear on joints, more work for heart and lungs delivering raw materials and oxygen to larger numbers of body cells, greater increase in infection particularly after operations etc. There are likely to be more aches and pains carrying the extra weight, painful feet make movement more painful, so more sitting around leads to weight gain and a vicious circle develops.

People in this type of cycle tend not to feel very good about themselves and this in turn can lead to depression, anxiety and other mental health problems. On the other hand, people on a well-balanced diet are far more likely to enjoy exercise and become fitter. As a result they are less likely to get infections and suffer from mental health problems so are more healthy.

It is far healthier to be thin than fat, but, moderation in all things. People, (more often but not always, young women), may go to the other extreme with eating disorders, starving and bingeing. These are mental health problems, again associated with poor self image; sufferers resist treatment and require specialist help. Although they are painfully thin, sufferers think of themselves as fat so they starve more.

People who are underweight will often suffer from tiredness, anaemia, weakness and inability to fight infections. This is because a poor diet deprives the body of the nutrients it needs to stay fit and healthy. The health of the hair, skin, nails and bones may be badly affected too.

People in poor circumstances may have to eat less food in order to pay household bills. This may happen particularly with parents if they are giving the food they can afford to the young children in the family.

ELEMENT 6.2

Investigate balanced diets for clients with different needs

At the end of this Element you should have portfolio evidence which

- describes the nutritional needs of different people
- identifies factors which influence the diet patterns of different groups
- identifies factors affecting diet choice
- identifies nutritional requirements of special diets.

NUTRITIONAL NEEDS OF DIFFERENT CLIENT GROUPS

What are nutritional needs? You investigated this in Element 6.1. We are talking about the food groups such as protein, fat etc. and also recommended daily intakes of certain substances. We are concerned with different client groups such as children, active and non-active adults, pregnant women and older people.

Children

Many parents worry too much about their child's food intake. Others need to give a little more thought to the type of food eaten. The dietary 'advice' from NACNE and COMA mentioned in Element 6.1 applies to all individuals mentioned in this element as well. However, some of these individuals need special attention over and above this advice. Children use a lot of energy and they are growing fast. A child's size in comparison with an adult's, might make you think that about half the food requirement or similar is needed. This is not so; a child of seven to eight years needs nearly as much energy, protein and B group vitamins as an adult. Calcium requirement is greater because of the demands of the growing skeleton and teeth.

Young children should eat wholesome food which is satisfying and not usually be eating junk foods which provide lots of easily consumed kilojoules without filling the stomach for long. Children have a much larger skin surface compared to the volumes of their bodies, this means they lose heat much more rapidly and have to use more of their food intake to keep up their body temperature.

It is important to work out how much energy a child's diet should provide, and what are the RDIs which should be observed (usually protein, calcium, iron, vitamins A, C and D and plenty of bread, potatoes, meat, milk and cereals to supply B group vitamins, important for healthy development).

If you are caring for a child, make sure there is a wide variety of food groups available. Table 6.2.1 gives you these figures for some age groups.

Student activity 6

- In your summer holidays, you are looking after a three-year-old boy and his nine-year-old sister for two weeks. Your duties involve planning, preparing and supervising breakfast, lunch and the evening meal for the two children and their granny who is 78 years old and not at all active.
- Describe the nutritional needs of these individuals and say what type of things will influence what they choose to eat and how their food intake is altered by their activities, age or gender.

Our 'standard' individual in Element 6.1 referred to a fairly active adult male, and someone similar, but far less active (sitting around a great deal) needs far less in the way of energy and would be best to reduce the total quantity of fat they eat, particularly fat from animal sources. Adults should also be careful to watch the amount of tea, coffee, fizzy drinks and alcohol. Women tend to be smaller and less muscular than men and so they require slightly less of everything except

Gender	Age	Energy req. kJ		Protein req. g	Calcium mg	Iron mg	Vit A µg	Vit C mg	Vit D µg
Male 300	1 300	5000 20	4500 20	30 10	27 10	600	600	7	7
Females 300	2 300	5750 20	5500 20	35 10	32 10	600	600	7	7
300	3–4 300	6500 20	6250 20	39 10	37 10	600	600	8	8
300	5–6 300	7250 20	7000 20	43 10	42 10	600	600	10	10
400	7–8 400	8250 20	8000 20	49 –	48	600	600	10	10
575	9–11 575	9500 25	8500 25	56 –	51	700	700	12	12
725	12–14 725	11000 25	9000 25	66 –	53	700	700	12	12
750	15–17 750	12000 30	9000 30	72 –	53	600	600	12	12

Table 6.2.1 *Nutritional requirements of children per day*

iron. During their fertile years (say 11–55 years of age) women have menstrual bleeding every month. Most women, for this reason, are slightly anaemic (their red blood cells cannot carry quite as much oxygen as they might). Extra iron helps the body to make up for the loss of blood in menstruation. After the fertile years, the need for iron returns to being the same as it is for males.

Pregnant women

What about pregnant women, do they count as two individuals? The answer is no. For much of the pregnancy the baby is too tiny to make any difference and later on it is important that the woman does not put on too much weight. What she does need is extra protein to make new cells as the baby grows, extra calcium and vitamin D to form the bones in the skeleton and teeth, extra energy supplies to help her carry the baby and for the baby's activity. She will also need plenty of vitamins and minerals for a healthy body and to allow the baby to develop in the correct way.

Older people

The range of activity of older people is very large – some are fairly inactive while others are very active, and so their needs vary widely too. An inactive person may need much less in the way of food requirements to avoid the danger of becoming overweight. Protein is needed less too, as hardly any growth is taking place and repair is fairly slow. Vitamins and minerals are just as important in later as in earlier years.

WHAT INFLUENCES FOOD HABITS?

We have already mentioned age and gender and how they affect food intake. The type of work and leisure activities people are involved in is important too. All the way through looking at diets we have mentioned the degree of activity involved, here is no exception. The squash player, the porter, the footballer, the ballet dancer all use massive amounts of energy which can only be supplied from the diet. Whereas the television addict, the typist, the needleworker and the bank clerk use very little energy at work, so usually need less carbohydrate and fat.

WHAT INFLUENCES OUR CHOICE OF FOOD?

While individuals have similar food requirements, these can be met in hundreds of different ways by combining food groups. Choice of food is influenced by social, economic and cultural factors. Most big events in our lives are celebrated by people getting together for a meal. Weddings, funerals, christenings and bar mitzvahs for example are all marked by families and friends joining together for meals. Three other factors influencing choice are listed in Figure 42. Join with two or three of your group and discuss some of the ideas mentioned under the three headings.

Special diets are certain patterns of eating certain foods for a special reason.

Weight reducing diets

If food intake is greater than energy output, then energy will be stored in cells in the form of glycogen (stored carbohydrate) and fat. Over a period of time, this storage will lead to an increase in body weight and the person may decide to begin a weight reducing diet. The most effective way of losing weight is to eat less food and increase output in the form of activity or exercise. These types of diets must still contain vitamins and minerals, protein and some energy requirements. It is most effective over a longer period of time if habits are changed permanently, e.g. grill foods instead of frying them, finish off with fresh fruit instead of puddings.

Student activity 7

- Obtain one or two samples of weight reducing diets from magazines.
- In groups of two or three discuss each diet in terms of its effectiveness and nutritional value.
- Write up your discussion or ask your tutor to video tape the session for evidence.

Diabetic diets

By telling people with diabetes to follow a special 'diabetic' diet, medical advisers are trying to make sure clients with this condition lead as normal a life as possible while

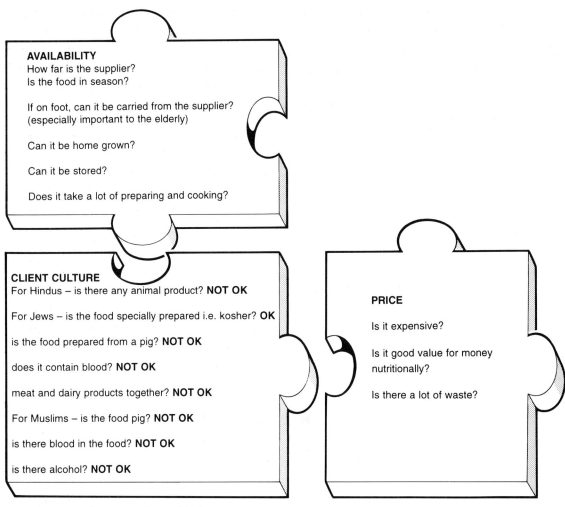

AVAILABILITY
How far is the supplier?
Is the food in season?

If on foot, can it be carried from the supplier?
(especially important to the elderly)

Can it be home grown?

Can it be stored?

Does it take a lot of preparing and cooking?

CLIENT CULTURE
For Hindus – is there any animal product? **NOT OK**

For Jews – is the food specially prepared i.e. kosher? **OK**

is the food prepared from a pig? **NOT OK**

does it contain blood? **NOT OK**

meat and dairy products together? **NOT OK**

For Muslims – is the food pig? **NOT OK**

is there blood in the food? **NOT OK**

is there alcohol? **NOT OK**

PRICE

Is it expensive?

Is it good value for money
nutritionally?

Is there a lot of waste?

Figure 42   *Influences on choice of food*

keeping their blood sugar level fairly steady. Unchanging body weight, regular exercise, careful diet and medicines taken at the correct time intervals will all help to do this.

The carbohydrates in the diet must be spaced out at regular intervals – meals should not be missed otherwise medicines do not work properly and blood sugar levels go up and down rather wildly. Diabetic people are taught how to test their own urine for sugar (so they can estimate how much sugar they have in their blood) and change their carbohydrate intake to stabilise their blood sugar.

Vegetarian diets

Vegetarian diets are followed by people who eat milk and cheese but no slaughtered animal or fish products at all. Some vegetarians eat eggs as well. This might suggest that vegetarian diets are lacking in protein. This is not so, there are many plant sources of protein such as peas, beans, lentils, soya beans, nuts, rice, wheat etc. What is important, however, is that a vegetarian follows a mixed diet to ensure that all the different proteins required by the body are obtained. People, often teenagers, becoming vegetarian in a family of meat eaters, may through ignorance or lack of planning become short of vitamin B12 and/or iron. Plenty of leafy green vegetables and egg yolk should provide enough iron while vitamin B12 can be supplied by dairy products.

Vegan diets

Vegans avoid all animal products including honey and milk. Thus their diets are high in fibre and low in fat. Vegans usually have less risk of heart disease, diabetes and arthritis. A varied and balanced vegan diet will provide all the essential nutrients for most individu-

als, but some may need to take extra iron, vitamin B12 and calcium. Tofu or soya bean curd is a rich source of calcium and if vegans include this in their diet on a regular basis, there should be no low levels of calcium.

Student activity 8

- Interview one or two people who follow vegetarian and vegan diets, ask them to supply a list of the foods they eat regularly.
- Discuss any nutritional problems they might have had and how they have overcome them, or how they avoid nutritional problems by careful meal planning.
- If your interviewees do not plan carefully and have not experienced nutritional problems, investigate their daily diets and draw conclusions yourself.

ELEMENT 6.3

Plan and cost diets

This element expects you to be able to identify clients needs, produce and explain a plan to meet those needs, describe the nature and function of the content of the plan and lastly work out the cost of the plan. You should be able to do this for a child, adult and elder, all

from the UK or another culture, or someone with a special need. This sounds quite a lot, but you have already learned a lot about nutrition from the first two elements and you can use this knowledge to produce your plan.

At the end of this element you should have evidence for your portfolio which

- identifies different client needs
- produces a diet plan which meets client's needs

- describes the nutritional content of the plan and explains how it meets the client's needs
- describes how much each meal will cost and relates it to a budget.

No.	Food	Inedible waste %	Energy kcal	kJ	Protein g	Fat g	Carbohydrate (as mono-saccharide) g
	Fish						
41	White fish, filleted	3	77	324	17.1	0.9	0
42	Cod, fried	0	235	982	19.6	14.3	7.5
43	Fish fingers, raw	0	178	749	12.6	7.5	16.1
44	Herrings, whole	46	251	1,040	16.8	20.4	0
45	Mackerel	40	282	1,170	19.0	22.9	0
46	pilchards, canned in tomato sauce	0	126	531	18.8	5.4	0.7
47	Sardines, canned in oil, fish only	0	217	906	23.7	18.6	0
48	Tuna in oil	0	289	1,202	22.8	22.0	0
49	Prawns, boiled	0	107	451	22.6	1.8	0
	Eggs						
50	Eggs, boiled	12	147	612	12.3	10.9	0
51	Eggs, fried	0	232	961	14.1	19.5	0
	Fats						
52	Butter	0	740	3,041	0.4	82.0	0
53	Lard, cooking fat, dripping	0	892	3,667	0	99.1	0
54	Low fat spread	0	366	1,506	0	40.7	0
55	Margarine, average	0	730	3,000	0.1	81.0	0
56	Cooking and salad oil	0	899	3,696	0	99.9	0
	Preserves, etc.						
57	Chocolate, milk	0	529	2,214	8.4	30.3	59.4
58	Honey	0	288	1,229	0.4	0	76.4
59	Jam	0	262	1,116	0.5	0	69.2
60	Marmalade	0	261	1,114	0.1	0	69.5
61	Sugar, white	0	394	1,680	0	0	105.3
62	Syrup	0	298	1,269	0.3	0	79.0
63	Peppermints	0	392	1,670	0.5	0.7	102.2
	Vegetables						
64	Aubergines	23	14	62	0.7	0	3.1
65	Baked beans	0	81	345	4.8	0.6	15.1
66	Beans, runner, boiled	1	19	83	1.9	0.2	2.7
67	Beans, red kidney, raw	0	272	1,159	22.1	1.7	45.0
68	Beans, soya, boiled	0	141	592	12.4	6.4	9.0
69	Beetroot, boiled	0	44	189	1.8	0	9.9
70	Brussels sprouts, boiled	0	18	75	2.8	0	1.7
71	Cabbage, raw	43	22	92	2.8	0	2.8
72	Cabbage boiled	0	15	66	1.7	0	2.3
73	Carrots, old	4	23	98	0.7	0	5.4
74	Cauliflower, cooked	0	9	40	1.6	0	0.8
75	Celery	27	8	36	0.9	0	1.3
76	Courgettes, raw	13	29	122	1.6	0.4	5.0

Table 6.3.1   *Composition of food per 100g*

m	Iron mg	Sodium mg	Vitamin A (retinol equivalent) µg	Thiamin mg	Riboflavin mg	Niacin equivalent mg	Vitamin C mg	No.
	0.5	99	1	0.07	0.09	6.0	0	41
	0.5	100	0	0.06	0.07	4.9	0	42
	0.7	320	0.2	0.09	0.06	3.5	0	43
	0.8	67	46	0	0.18	7.2	0	44
	1.0	130	45	0.09	0.35	11.6	0	45
	2.7	370	8	0.02	0.29	11.1	0	46
	2.9	650	7	0.04	0.36	12.6	0	47
	1.1	420	0	0.04	0.11	17.2	0	48
	1.1	1,590	0	0.03	0.03	7.4	0	49
	2.0	140	190	0.09	0.47	3.7	0	50
	2.5	220	140	0.07	0.42	4.2	0	51
	0.2	870	985	0	0	0.1	0	52
	0.1	2	0	0	0	0	0	53
	0	690	900	0	0	0	0	54
	0.3	800	860	0	0	0.1	0	55
	0	0	0	0	0	0	0	56
	1.6	120	6.6	0.10	0.23	1.6	0	57
	0.4	11	0	0	0.05	0.2	0	58
	1.2	14	2	0	0	0	10	59
	0.6	18	8	0	0	0	10	60
	0	0	0	0	0	0	0	61
	1.5	270	0	0	0	0	0	62
	0.2	9	0	0	0	0	0	63
	0.4	3	0	0.05	0.03	1.0	5	64
	1.4	550	12	0.08	0.06	1.3	0	65
	0.7	1	67	0.03	0.07	0.8	5	66
	6.7	40	0	0.54	0.18	5.5	0	67
	2.5	15	0	0.26	0.16	3.4	0	68
	0.4	64	0	0.02	0.04	0.4	5	69
	0.5	2	67	0.06	0.10	0.9	40	70
	0.6	7	50	0.06	0.05	0.8	55	71
	0.4	4	50	0.03	0.03	0.5	20	72
	0.6	95	2,000	0.06	0.05	0.7	6	73
	0.4	4	5	0.06	0.06	0.8	20	74
	0.6	140	0	0.03	0.03	0.5	7	75
	1.5	1	58	0.05	0.09	0.6	16	76

Identifying different client needs

The basic information for this is to be found in Element 2, so we will go into detail here and produce a plan for two individual clients. You can then choose someone you know and try some of these tasks for yourself by working out a menu for them. Remember to base it on what they like to eat, what is good for them, and how much you have to spend. Ask your tutor to help you.

Student activity 9

- You are looking after Julie, a nine-year-old girl for two weeks in your Summer holidays and also preparing meals for her granny and younger brother. Julie is a very active girl, she likes horse riding and has her own pony to exercise. Because of her love for animals, Julie will not eat meat of any kind although she will eat dairy products. She could be called a vegetarian. Granny likes her meat and insists on having meat and two vegetables once every day. She has some difficulty chewing and likes small pieces of food and small meals fairly often, she also insists on British food and will not even try 'any foreign dishes'. Fortunately, James, the youngest, likes all sorts of food and will fit in with most ideas. On this occasion, we will not include James in our planning.

  Julie's mother has given you £30 to pay for breakfast, lunch and evening meal for five days.

It is a good idea when faced with a problem like this to talk to the individuals concerned. Make a list of the things you need to know from them. Does it include

- When do they like their main meal – lunchtime or evening? Julie said she did not mind but Granny does not like a heavy meal in the evening. You note that the main meal will be lunch.
- What are their favourite foods? Julie likes cheese, eggs and salad meals. Granny prefers hot meals midday, and nutritious snacks at other times.
- What foods do they not like at all? On a budget you cannot afford to waste money buying foods they will not eat! Julie hates tinned tomatoes, fried eggs, kidney beans. Granny does not like foods with seeds in – they get in the cracks between her false teeth. Otherwise she has been brought up to eat most foods.

Now you have a much broader picture of what you can buy and prepare. You have also found out by careful questioning that Granny is fairly unsteady on her feet, and she has a taxi twice a week to go to church and to see her other daughter a few miles away. She is therefore not very active.

JULIE'S NEEDS

- 8500kJ carbohydrates and fat
- protein 51g
- calcium 700mg
- iron 12mg
- vitamins A 575µg, C 25mg, D, supplied by outdoor life (horseriding, action of sun on skin)
- fibre, plentiful from vegetarian diet
- minerals, plentiful from vegetarian diet. Julie should get plenty of vitamin B12 as she eats dairy produce and cereals.

GRANNY'S NEEDS

- 7000kJ supplied by carbohydrates and fat
- protein 42g
- calcium 500mg
- iron 10mg
- vitamins A 750µg, C 30mg, D (should we have asked in our previous chat whether anyone took extra supplements to their food, and if Granny went outdoors very much?

Mental note make sure there are vitamin D rich foods in Granny's diet plan).

You have identified nutritional needs and now you have to use these to make a plan of foods and menus. This requires the use of food tables but, if you have not got these you can use nutritional information on tins, packets and cartons. This will take longer to do. A food table analyses each food to show its component food groups. Table 6.3.1 shows an example from *The Manual of Nutrition*. Try to get the most up to date version that you can, you should be able to find these tables in libraries in reference sections.

You will have to take account of the quantity of food in the food table. For example, a boiled egg is usually quoted as composition per 100g of boiled egg – as you are well aware, people have one or two boiled eggs but not 100g. In this case you might need scales to weigh a typical boiled egg. But we do not eat shells do we? Experts would take off the weight of a shell but, it is the broad principles of diet planning we are concerned with here. A large egg with the shell on weighs nearly 100g but a smaller egg will only weigh between 60g and 80g.

Looking then at the food table entry for a 100g egg, we can find that an egg provides 612kJ of energy, 12.3g of protein, surprisingly 10.9g of fat (this contributes to the energy – remember 1g of fat provides 37kJ of energy), 0g carbohydrate, 52mg calcium, 2mg of iron, 190µg of vitamin A and no vitamin C at all.

There is also no fibre in an egg – it would not be very good to live on eggs alone then, there is no carbohydrate to help with energy requirements and no vitamin C to resist disease. In fact, like many sailors on long voyages in years gone by, an individual, in due course, would develop scurvy – a fatal disease caused by lack of vitamin C.

Anyway, we are well on the way to supplying many nutrients, and see what happens if we add two slices of buttered wholemeal toast.

One slice of bread weighs about 30g and butter or spread for one slice is between 7g to 10g.

100g of wholemeal bread contains 911kJ, 9g protein, 2.5g fat, 42g carbohydrate, 54mg calcium, 3mg iron, and no vitamins A or C unless this has been specially added by the baker (look at the wrapper information). However, this was for 100g and we require 2 slices of bread each weighing 30g, which totals 60g or 60% of the figure quoted for 100g.

So energy for 2 slices of bread is

$$\frac{911 \times 60}{100} = 547kJ$$

Similarly for protein in 2 slices

$$\frac{9 \times 60}{100} = 5.4g$$

and so on for all the other components.

Now you can add these values to the egg values. Butter needs to be altered similarly, 100g of butter provides a massive 3041kJ of energy, but we only want say 16g, so the calculation this time is

$$3041 \times \frac{16}{100} = 487kJ$$

notice it nearly doubles the energy value of the bread. Add this to the egg and bread, perhaps you would include milk for Julie and tea for Granny and there you have a healthy breakfast for two people with all the nutritional values accounted for and easily costed by visiting a supermarket. Other different breakfasts might be porridge, Weetabix, toast and marmalade or fruit alone or with cereal. Five breakfasts all able to be calculated and taken from the overall daily allowance needed for health.

You may wish to continue with Julie or her grandmother for your evidence gathering or begin afresh with a client you are in contact with. Start by identifying the client's needs as we did with Julie and her grandmother.

Present your plan as a chart with columns

representing the five days in one direction and the meals and times in the other direction.

Refer back to Element 6.1 for the functions of the groups you have mentioned and why the individual concerned requires them. Finally, cost your plan and make sure it complies with the budget you have been given. Good Luck!

Reference
MAFF, *Manual of Nutrition*, London: HMSO.

7

EXPLORING HEALTH AND RECREATIONAL ACTIVITIES

When you are looking after people it is important that you should recognise that clients need some recreational activities to be well balanced and healthy people, just like you do. This chapter helps you to look at recreational activities available in your area, what benefits they provide and how they can meet clients' needs.

ELEMENT 7.1

Investigate health and recreational activities

At the end of this section, you should have

- identified suitable recreational activities for different client groups
- identified the benefits of recreational activities for the health and well-being of different client groups
- described common barriers to taking part in recreational activities
- suggested ways to overcome common barriers
- identified recreational activities available locally.

First of all, the client groups we shall concentrate on are children, teenagers or adolescents, elders and families.

Next, what type of activities are there? We can divide up the activities into

- physical – generally using muscular action to do the activity
- intellectual – using your brain in thinking or working things out
- social – meeting people, mixing with other people, talking and interacting with them.

Most recreational activities are mixtures of these, but usually one activity is more prominent than the others, e.g. playing in a rugby team is physical, intellectual (thinking about tactics) and social as you are constantly interacting with your team members on and off the rugby field. However, nearly everyone would agree that rugby is mainly a physical activity.

Swimming is a physical activity done alone without much thinking necessary.

Student activity 1

- Using a piece of flipchart paper and coloured marker pens draw up a table which has three columns labelled **physical**, **intellectual** and **social** benefits. Think of as many recreational activities as possible and write them on sticky notepaper (the sort people use in offices to add memos to documents).
- Let group members in turn place their note on the flip chart in the correct column for the main type of benefit resulting from that activity. The rest of the group discuss whether they agree with the decision.
- When the exercise is finished, everyone can copy down the agreed benefits of the activity.
- When your table is complete, think about the activities you have collected on the flip chart and say which client group you think the activity is suited to. There may be more than one answer. You could do this by writing about each one or more easily design either a colour code for each client group or place a large code letter against each note, e.g. C for children, A for adolescents, E for elders and F for families.

We have to consider the suitability of a recreational activity. It is no good suggesting swimming for a female member of a religious group who is not permitted to expose any parts of her body except the face. So culture is one factor to consider. What could others be?

Age should be a factor, e.g. most elders cannot take part in strenuous physical games, but can enjoy keep fit exercises to music using large bean bags or balls. The exercise helps to keep joints mobile, stimulates blood circulation, promotes social activity and the 'feel-good factor'. Similarly, young children have not the strength to undertake vigorous activity for long periods of time, but can be 'on the go' with one physical activity after another for what seems like a long time.

Most adolescents, however, have the ability to undergo moderate physical exercise for some time e.g. game of tennis, squash or netball. Physical activity throughout childhood and adolescence helps bones form their final adult shape, stimulates blood circulation and hormone release and generally promotes bodily health. Walking, snooker, darts, gardening are all reasonable physical activities that many elders undertake.

All ages love parties, opportunities to meet friends and have fun together, and the same goes for trips or outings. As a result, people develop a common interest for discussion, reminiscence, have the opportunity to dress up and look special, while enjoying a change of scene. Discussions are particularly hard to keep going in a residential setting for elders, many cannot concentrate for long, some fall asleep, others have no interest in anyone else's views.

Adolescents on the other hand love to debate and argue both past and current issues, while children find it difficult to concentrate on talking about the same subject for too long. Families often hold discussions at mealtimes, but mealtimes as family occasions do seem to be declining, many adolescents prefer fast food with their friends, and often a parent is working antisocial hours.

Fitness is another factor determining the suitability of recreational activities for people. Even unfit adolescents should not undertake strenuous physical exercise without some training beforehand. Several people each year get into serious life-threatening difficulties because they undertake dangerous activities without correct preparation, suitable equipment and training by professionals. Elders and children are less likely to get

Figure 43   *Swimming is a physical activity, rather than an intellectual or a social one*

into trouble in this way, but families on a day out might become carried away with enthusiasm, because one member has some experience of the activity.

Gender is becoming less and less important in suitability of recreation. We now have plenty of female football and rugby teams, female wrestlers, snooker players and golfers. A few years ago, many of these would have been unheard of, but today there are many examples. Some males knit, crochet and sew, but on the whole these activities seem less acceptable to male client groups than females carrying out male recreational activities. With older people, it is probably less acceptable to suggest an activity per-

ceived as the 'property' of the other gender, e.g. females undertaking a 'masculine' activity such as snooker. Younger people are not prone to such stereotyping.

The last important factor is budget. If you cannot afford the fees of the local country club, then there is no point in applying to join. Do not aim to take up golf, if the only golf course around has a large joining fee and annual subscription, you have no wage and therefore limited finances.

It has already been mentioned that it is foolish and often dangerous to attempt some activities without being correctly fitted out, e.g. rock climbing without suitable footwear. You will be able to think of many other

Figure 44   *Females taking on an activity traditionally seen as a 'male' activity*

examples; getting properly equipped takes money for hire or purchase.

Costs are a major barrier to many people taking up recreational activities which they would at least like to try. Hiring equipment is a cheaper short-term answer to purchasing but not in the long term. Club membership can be cheaper than paying on each occasion and discounts or concessions are often available for the unwaged, regular users, senior citizens or students, so it is well worth investigating the possibilities. There are often open days or opportunities to try unusual activities at festivals and shows. Still it has to be said that the costs involved do mean many people are seriously disadvantaged.

Student activity 2

- Examine you local newspaper (free ones are often the best for this) and collect cuttings about concessions, open days etc.
- If you live close to your local library, pay them a visit and find out if they keep a display of information about local recreational activities. You may be able to pick up some leaflets.
- Write to two or three clubs and ask if they have reduced costs or fees for certain client groups.
- Write a report about your findings for your portfolio.

Actually getting into a place where recreation is being carried out can be extremely difficult or impossible for some client groups. Even when getting in is not a problem other barriers may arise.

People with hearing difficulties may not be able to hear anything as they are so far away from the sounds. Stairs or absence of lifts may prevent people from getting to the right area. Corridors may not be wide enough for wheelchair users to move around safely. Fire regulations might interfere with the rights of wheelchair users to use the facilities, in case there is an obstruction when evacuating others.

Toilet facilities may be very limited particularly at shows and other outdoor events and totally impossible for wheelchair users. There may be age restrictions to some activities, children may not be allowed in, this bars families with young children, so the adults cannot participate either unless child care facilities are provided.

Finally, access to the activity may be provided but transport is the main problem. Cars, buses and trains are often inaccessible to people with mobility problems.

However, the news is not always gloomy, more and more people and organisations are adapting their premises to make them attractive and accessible to all. Transport providers are gradually changing some of their facilities and particularly, if they are given warning of disabled or elderly clients' travel plans, they can help a great deal. Leaflets are published to assist the disabled client.

Student activity 3

- Choose two recreational activities you might wish to do away from home.
- Investigate how you could get to the activity if first you used a wheelchair, and second, if you were blind and had a guide dog to assist you.
- What problems would you meet once you got there?
- Using your survey skills from Element 7.2, suggest ways of overcoming these barriers. You may need to interview the managers of a recreational facility to find out what adaptations, if any, they were planning to make in the future so that different client groups could access the facility.
- Find out how much change or adaptation has already been carried out. Can you think of any other ways facilities could be altered?

ELEMENT 7.2

Survey the use of local recreational activities

At the end of this section you should have

- identified the location and opening hours of local centres providing recreational activities
- identified the main groups of clients using local recreational activities
- identified the main characteristics of clients of local recreational activities
- described the activities available to clients at local centres
- identified the patterns of use of the local centres by different client groups
- identified the benefits to clients of the activities
- described any barriers to client participation at the local centres.

The first thing you should do is find the information you got together for Element 1.1 and use the parts on recreational activities to help you with this Element. Some of the work for Element 2.1 on 'green spaces' and 'leisure facilities' will also be helpful.

Student activity 4

This Element asks you to look at what recreational facilities there are in your home area. The best way to do this is by finding out what facilities there are, and then going to look at what they have to offer.

- As a group, make a list of all the places for recreation you know in your town or your area. Where are the swimming pools, parks, public football fields, pool halls, and library? Where are the pubs? What sort of different activities do they have there – are some more suitable for families and some for young people? Are there discos, quiz nights or theme nights?
- Are there places where people can go for walks, such as along the canal or the river bank?
- Do you know of any clubs, such as a chess club, or judo, diving, rock climbing, caving? Ask at the library if they have a list of local clubs.
- Once you have your complete list of leisure and recreational activities and local clubs, put down these headings

  children
  adolescents
  elders
  families
  groups
  special needs

- Under each of these headings, put down the leisure and recreational facilities which you think would be most appropriate for each one. Some of the things will appear in more than one list, pubs might be fine for everyone, except children without adults, and so might swimming.
- Using the PIES information from Chapter 2, decide which need is being met by each of these activities. Do the exercises on PIES again if you need to remind yourself about what they are.
- Find a map of your area, and mark on it where all the places are that you identified as leisure and recreational facilities, giving them all numbers as a key (see Figure 45 for an example).
- When you have done this, make a guide to the places, giving information about each one. For example:

  1 Swimming pool, Church Street.
  Open every day from 10am to 9pm, except Sunday, when it is open 10am to 6pm entry £1.20.
  Has sessions for families, elders, and children. Also a disabled swimming club, and life-saving lessons.
  2 Park and boating lake, off Park Road.
  Park open every day from dawn until dusk.
  Boating lake boat hire from 11am to 7pm daily from April to October.
  Rowing boats £1 for half an hour, pedal boats 50p for 15 minutes.
  3 Sports centre, Dansdale Gardens, off Queen Street.
  Squash courts, indoor and outdoor tennis, weight training and sauna.
  Open from 7am to 11pm every day.
  Has a judo club, tumble tots, aerobics, climbing wall and a creche.
  Payment is for individual activities, or an annual fee of £420 allowing access to everything.

Continue with your list in a similar way to this, covering all the places you have found.

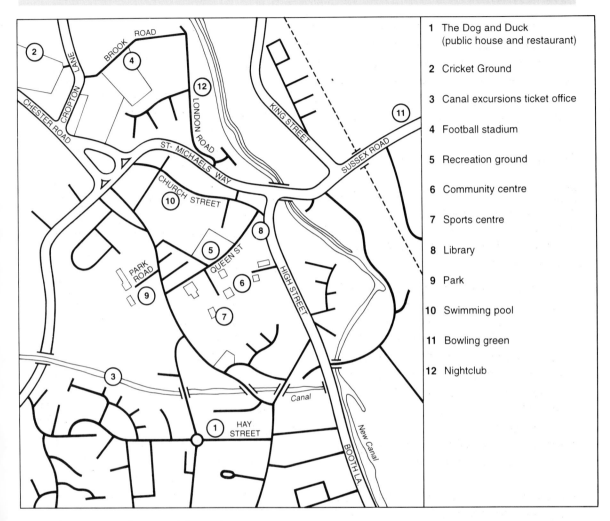

Figure 45   *Map of town with key to show amenities*

BARRIERS

One or two barriers to using these facilities have already been mentioned. Not many places will let children in if they do not have an adult with them. Some places have age restrictions, such as over-16s only; or over-25s only. A creche is only for very young children and you must have special needs to go to some of the clubs provided for them.

When you find out about amenities, you may need to think about some of the following questions. How easy are the places to get to? Are there buses that go there? How much is the fare from the town centre? Other activities require you to be very active and fit, such as the climbing wall, scuba diving and caving, parachuting or hang gliding. What is the access to these facilities like for people with a physical disability? Remember that if somewhere is accessible to a wheelchair, it will be accessible to other people with walking problems, or with parents pushing a pram or pushchair. Are there many steps, or revolving doors at the entrance, or once inside? Is the lift big enough for a wheelchair, and can someone sitting down reach the buttons? Are the buttons marked in braille so that a blind person can use them?

The barrier to some activities is the expense. Some leisure clubs charge an annual membership of hundreds of pounds, and so do some golf clubs. Other activities require special equipment, such as sub-aqua diving, hand gliding and parachuting, and motor racing. You may also have to travel a long way to get to them. There are not many motor racing circuits in the country, and horse racing is only available in a few towns. Some activities such as horse riding or judo require special clothing, which can be quite expensive.

Student activity 5

• When you have identified the places people go to for leisure and recreation, visit some of them and find out who the main users (or client groups) are. Are they mostly teenagers or old people? Are there particular times of day when mothers and young children are there, or older people? This is looking at the pattern of usage.

• Choose one of the places and ask the staff about the pattern of usage because you will not be able to watch all the time the place is open or go every day. The staff will have a good idea of what goes on, it is up to you to ask them the right questions. Ask them questions about the people who use the facility, what times of day and what days are busier than others. Are some times of the year busier than others?

• What do you and the staff think is the reason for this pattern of usage?

• What is the benefit of the facility to the people who use it?

• What are the barriers to participation? Is it very expensive? Is it difficult to get to? Do the users need to bring any special equipment or clothing? Is it accessible to people with disabilities?

• Write all this up in the form of a report for your portfolio.

ELEMENT 7.3

Suggested recreational activities for clients with specific needs

At the end of this section you will have

• identified the specific needs of different client groups
• identified factors influencing the recreational activities available to different client groups

• suggested recreational activities which meet the specific needs and taken into account influencing factors
• described the main health and safety factors for the suggested activities
• described the benefits of the activities for the client groups.

The three client groups with which we are concerned in the Element are slightly different to those we have concerned ourselves with in the other two Elements. This time we shall consider clients with physical disabilities, those clients who have problems of obesity, and elders.

CLIENTS WITH PHYSICAL DISABILITIES

What needs might clients with physical disabilities have? Certainly a need to keep fit, possibly much fitter than those without disabilities because generally, it means that a client often has to use more energy to overcome the difficulty. There is a saying in the caring profession 'use it or lose it' and this is very true for these clients and those who are elderly.

Remember that a client with a physical disability may also be elderly. There is a need therefore to focus on the things a client can do, not on the things they cannot do. When you are caring for someone, be positive about their achievements, however small. Your encouragement will help them to try harder.

An important factor is the possibility that a client who has some degree of immobility could very easily become a client with a problem of obesity, so adding to their difficulties. So, it is important to keep them as physically active as possible to minimise effort and prevent obesity. Joints and muscles capable of function need to be exercised regularly to maintain that function.

There is also the feel-good factor of independence and being able to exercise choice;

even more important when you may require assistance in some areas. Physically disabled clients, often now called, much more appropriately, 'differently abled clients', have the right to participate in as full a life as anyone else and this should include recreational activities. Segregation should be a thing of the past and socially there should be complete acceptance.

Sadly, although many people have a changed attitude, there are still a lot of people who think that differently abled people should be treated in a different way to everyone else. Socially, there should be no difference in recreational activities, their needs are the same as yours. Intellectual recreational activities are no different either; differently abled clients can often be much better at 'thinking' activities than the rest of us.

CLIENTS WITH A PROBLEM OF OBESITY

As emphasised previously, we all have physical, social and intellectual needs – because a client is overweight compared to our cultural norm (consider a Japanese sumo wrestler, looked on as a hero in his own culture) their needs are not any different. If a client is unhealthy and wishes to lose weight, then there might be a need to increase physical recreational activity rather than social (which often includes extra eating and drinking). Some excessively overweight people can become less active socially, for many reasons. Some of these might include

- people staring or making unkind remarks
- difficulty in obtaining suitable clothes for the occasion

Figure 46   *Sumo wrestlers are admired in their own culture*

- difficulty in moving around
- lack of comfort in seating
- not wanting to be seen in public.

On the other hand, many overweight people often carry on the most active lives socially and intellectually (and sometimes physically) and are the life and soul of a party. All this depends on the individual and we must be careful not to stereotype (this is when you expect an overweight person to behave as a social outcast and a 'couch potato').

Generally, a person becomes overweight when their energy intake is greater than their energy output, so increasing physical activity and therefore burning up the extra energy should cause a person to lose weight.

Alternatively, there may be medical problems which have led to obesity.

CLIENTS WHO ARE ELDERLY

Older clients have all three needs as the other groups did. Often, by necessity, physical activities need to be more gentle, and intellectual activities of shorter duration as the client gets older, but they all need to be there. Everyone has individual needs which can be met by a healthy balance of the three types of activities. As we discussed in Element 7.1, most recreational activities are a mixture.

Student activity 6

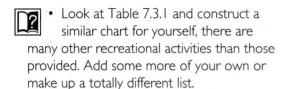 • Look at Table 7.3.1 and construct a similar chart for yourself, there are many other recreational activities than those provided. Add some more of your own or make up a totally different list.

• Place a tick in the columns where you think the activity is most likely to be most appropriate to the client group, a cross if you think it would only be the exceptional client who might accomplish the activity and a question mark if you think it really would not address the main need of that group.

Recreational activities	Clients with physical disabilities	Clients with a problem of obesity	Clients who are elderly
Physical activities			
Keep fit exercises			
Walking			
Playing snooker/pool			
Swimming			
Hockey			
Athletics			
Rugby			
Gardening			
Social activities			
Parties			
Outings/visits			
Whist/Beetle drives			
Family gatherings			
Luncheon clubs			
Discussion groups			
Dancing			
Singing groups			
Charades/board games			
Intellectual activities			
Reading			
Chess			
Listening to Music			
Painting			

Table 7.3.1 *Recreational activities*

You need to take influencing factors into consideration while you are doing this exercise.

TIME

An older client and an overweight client are unlikely to be able to keep up vigorous physical activity for long periods of time. Chess may be too long for most older clients to concentrate whereas draughts is a much shorter game. Beetle drives can take an afternoon to play as there are two sides to a game sheet and twelve games on each sheet, but reading can be tailored to suit the individual's concentration span.

MONEY

People on benefit or pensions are unlikely to afford specialist equipment or expensive fees so cheaper activities or those which are free, such as walking, are most suitable.

AVAILABILITY

If transport is a problem or there are no recreational facilities of the desired type in the area, then alternatives must be looked for. Before television was widely available, most families made their own entertainment through musical activities, reading, poetry, simple board or card games. These are nearly always available and can be used over and over again at very little cost.

PHYSICAL ABILITY

People unable to bend would be unlikely to undertake snooker or pool, but could enjoy swimming which is an excellent exercise for some clients who have problems moving around on land. Overweight clients are often excellent swimmers and can exercise freely in water because their lower limbs are not having to carry their excess weight.

ACCESS

We have already discussed the difficulty some people have with wheelchair access both into and within a building and overweight people with size and room given over to seating comfort. Older people might have difficulty in climbing stairs or be frightened of lifts and escalators. These fears often stop people participating in recreation and gradually they just stop going to the activity centre.

Student activity 7

- Write a short report on how you think some people might be encouraged and discouraged from participating in recreational activities because of the difficulties in access.

WHY SHOULD CLIENTS BOTHER WITH RECREATIONAL ACTIVITIES?

Here are some suggestions we have already made and some new ideas for you to consider in a summary form. Discuss them with your tutor and members of your group.

Recreational activities may give the opportunity to:

- improve mobility – joints and muscles
- stimulate blood circulation
- stimulate hormones
- increase strength

- increase stamina
- increase suppleness or flexibility
- feel good
- meet new people
- improve relationships
- discuss common interests
- enjoy life more
- be more creative
- save money by doing things yourself
- carry on learning
- develop new interests

You can probably add a few more to this list yourself.

Student activity 8

- Select four activities you mentioned in your chart of client groups and recreational activities and write a short account of the benefits clients would gain from those activities.

HEALTH AND SAFETY FACTORS

For many of the activities we have discussed, there are certain safety factors of which clients, or yourselves, should be aware. These could be grouped as hazards, risks, requirements and precautions.

Hazards are those dangers involved in an activity, whereas a risk is the possibility of something 'bad' happening. A requirement is the need to have some equipment or expert assistance available and a precaution something which any sensible person should do to prevent something bad happening.

Let us examine swimming as a recreational activity to illustrate these terms. Hazards of

swimming are drowning, head or spinal injury (if diving in), being swept out to sea. The risks associated with swimming if you are able to swim competently, you are not diving in, and you are in a swimming pool, are actually quite small. If you are a poor swimmer and in a sea with a strong current, and not observing sensible precautions, the risks are quite high.

The requirements for swimming in a pool, would be observation by a lifeguard attendant, and at sea, observe notices for swimmers.

Precautions to take in a pool, would be to notice the depths, stay within your own capabilities, wear buoyancy aids if needed and observe pool rules.

If at sea and you have doubts do not swim, ask advice, stay close to shore in own depth, let others know your intentions, do not stay too long, do not swim alone, use a buoyancy aid if needed, observe and obey all notices.

Here are a few tips for other recreational activities.

 • Do not overdo physical activity if you are not at the correct level of fitness. Pace yourself.
- Be prepared for extremes of weather.
- Take expert advice before starting.
- Ensure that you have the correct equipment, particularly footwear.
- Have first aid equipment with you and know what to do or take along first aiders.
- Make sure everyone complies with seat belt laws.
- Make sure people are aware of laws relating to driving and substance abuse.
- Is equipment working correctly and regularly tested?
- Do you know the rules of the activity?

- Let people know your intentions, expected time of arrival.
- Let people know who is in the party.
- Insurance has been taken out if necessary.
- Always clear up after you, take litter home.
- Is medication needed by some clients? Keep it safe.
- Is access organised for differently abled clients?
- Are there any hazards relating to electricity or gas?
- Are there any fire restrictions you need to know?
- Correctly stow wheelchairs, walking frames etc.

- Is lighting and ventilation adequate for the task?
- Is the activity too much for some clients?
- Consider the risks of falls, injuries.
- Have you sufficient helpers for the activity?

Again, you can probably think of others to add to this list.

Student activity 9

- Using the activities you selected in activity 8, write a report on the main health and safety factors which need to be considered for clients undertaking those activities.

8

EXPLORING PHYSICAL CARE

This unit is about the sort of help some people require with their day-to-day activities and how that help is given.

Investigate the provision of physical assistance

At the end of this section you should have

- identified and given examples of clients who might need physical help
- described the physical help that clients might need with activities in their daily life
- described safe lifting techniques
- described ways of continuing client independence and dignity
- described ways of identifying when clients need physical help.

CLIENTS WHO MIGHT REQUIRE PHYSICAL HELP

If you were asked to say who might need your physical assistance you would almost certainly mention elderly people. However, you must never assume because someone looks old they need help.

Many disabled and older people are fiercely independent and would be greatly offended if you automatically went to give help. If the client is in residential accommodation this may mean they have a greater degree of dependence than a client living in their own home. But, remember, some clients are in residential accommodation for very different reasons. It is always wise to assume each client is physically capable of managing their own daily activities and alter what you do to suit each individual. It is also worth noting that setbacks in physical ability can be temporary and full independence can be regained after a short period e.g. broken bones.

When you start caring for people you are often so eager to help that it is hard to curb your instincts. Most elderly people have lived in their own homes for many years before coming into care. They were used to making their own choices, meals, beds, entertainment, doing their hair, washing, shopping and so on. Most would have lived alone or perhaps with another similarly aged person. Think how you would feel suddenly moving into a home, with staff to look after you, and other people all around.

Kindly staff probably pay a great deal of attention to a new resident when most of all they would like some peace and quiet to adapt to new surroundings and possibly mourn the passing of their old ways and independence.

Elderly people then, of course, must be mentioned if we are giving examples of clients who need physical assistance, but there are many others, in fact we certainly could not mention them all, and you will assist a lot of people who are not mentioned here!

Clients with restricted mobility means people who cannot move around as well as we can. Arthritis is a disease of joints which is very common. People suffer pain, swelling and stiffness which restricts movement. There are several types of arthritis, but there are two main types.

Osteoarthritis affects more people than any other form of arthritis. It is caused through wear and tear on the joints (usually the large joints such as hip and knee) so mostly affects people in their later middle age and old age. Rheumatoid arthritis affects people at a younger age than osteoarthritis and more women than men. The joints are very painful, swollen and stiff and as the disease progresses many joints (usually the smaller joints at the wrist, hands and feet) become severely deformed.

Joints can be affected by other disorders such as haemophilia. This is a bleeding disorder, the blood cannot clot properly on its own. Children who have this disease usually inherit it from one of their parents and suffer bleeds into their joints and muscles as well as other places in the body. This causes painful deformity unless special treatment is given promptly.

Fractures of bones involving joints can lead to restricted movement and the onset of early osteoarthritis.

There is a group of diseases which affects the nerves which control muscles and therefore affects 'motor' skills. We use the term 'motor' to mean anything that brings about movement – in this case, muscles or nerves which control muscles. This group of diseases is called motor neurone disease (a neurone is a nerve cell) and can be inherited, affecting children or coming later in life, affecting mainly men over fifty.

Disorders of the brain can affect motor skills and the ability to receive sensations from the outside world. Some examples of clients with brain disorders who may need physical assistance are

- children and adults with learning difficulties and physical disabilities
- those who have suffered head injury, meningitis, abscess or tumour
- those who have developed degenerative disorders such as Alzheimers disease or Parkinsons disease.

There are also cerebrovascular disorders or what we all call strokes. The causes of strokes can be a clot forming in an artery (about 50% of all strokes), a bleed from a weak blood vessel (about 25% of all strokes) or a fragment of a clot from elsewhere in the

Figure 47   *Never pre-judge someone because of their age – exercise classes can be useful for old or young people*

body which is pumped round by the heart and gets stuck in a small blood vessel of the brain. This is called an embolism (about 25% of all strokes). It is usually extremely difficult to tell the exact cause when the damage occurs, which is why doctors and nurses tend to call these illnesses cerebrovascular (brain blood vessel) accidents, often called CVAs.

The extent of the damage and its effect on the client depend on how large the blocked blood vessel is, whether any blood can get to that part of the brain by any other route and where in the brain the blockage occurs. It is not so much that the blood vessel is blocked, but more that that part of the brain may not receive any oxygen from the blood and therefore die. If the part is large or is a very important area the person may lose consciousness and die. On the other hand, the client may barely notice the symptoms – about 33% of all strokes result in death, another 33% result in some disability, while the remaining 34% recover completely.

If the CVA involves the part of the brain known as the motor area, the client may have muscular weakness or paralysis on one side of the body. If it affects the most powerful side of the brain, (we all have one side more dominant than the other) speech may be lost or slurred, and if it affects an area behind the motor area, sensation may be lost, i.e. the part feels numb to the touch.

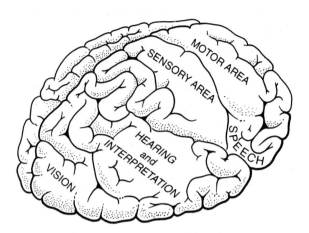

Figure 48   *Motor, sensory and speech areas of the brain*

This numbness can be a form of sensory impairment. Blindness, partial sight, deafness and partial deafness, loss of smell are also forms of sensory impairment.

All these clients may require physical assistance at some time of the day or night. The assistance you may need to give them in their daily routine might involve helping them cook food, feed themselves, get dressed or undressed or have a bath.

Student activity I

- If you work either voluntarily or as an employee in a care establishment choose two clients who need physical help from you or another assistant. Write two short accounts of why each client needs help and what physical help each client needs to carry out everyday activities such as cooking, feeding, dressing and bathing.
- If you do not have the opportunity to find this information direct, then ask a care assistant to talk to you about the sort of help some clients need. However, in both cases

remember confidentiality and avoid real names and anything else which might identify the clients.

COOKING

Clients who need help to carry out cooking should be encouraged to do so in a safe environment, very often this will mean that you will give help but not take over. Special potato peelers and tap turners are available for those with limited movement in their upper limbs, so it is possible for clients to keep skills like these for much longer if suitable aids are obtained. If a client has sensory loss, it is particularly important to watch that they do not burn or cut themselves because sometimes they may be unaware they have hurt themselves. Kitchens may need to be specially designed so that storage areas, cookers, sinks and food preparing surfaces are lower than normal if the client uses a wheelchair or needs to sit down to do these tasks.

Redesigning the layout of a kitchen should also be considered if someone has less movement or poor motor skills so that they do not have to constantly cross backwards and forwards to obtain materials. Advice can be offered regarding easy meals to cook, but a client should have food of their own choosing whenever possible. Religious and cultural considerations should be respected at all times but particularly with diet. Lightweight saucepans with heatproof handles will reduce the weight to be carried and there are also devices allowing pans, bowls and teapots to be tipped safely. Clients will develop a greater sense of independence if they can cook one or two simple meals with assistance.

Elderly clients may forget to turn heat off

or on, forget they have left something cooking and if they have lost their sense of smell as well (one of the earliest senses to fade) put themselves and others at risk of fire. This should not mean they are prevented from cooking, but should be supervised in a quiet way.

FEEDING

Clients who have nervous disorders and strokes often have difficulty swallowing and chewing. Other clients may not have the power or flexibility in their upper limbs to be truly independent at meal times.

Some simple tips when helping clients to eat:

- Keep meals attractive and tasty – when eating is difficult it is often tempting to give up after a short time so you need to encourage clients to eat.
- Keep mealtimes easy and comfortable, if you are helping do not appear to be in a hurry.
- Use ordinary cutlery and offer food in small amounts.
- Make sure each mouthful has been swallowed before offering the next by allowing plenty of time between mouthfuls.
- If a client uses false teeth or dentures make sure these are in place and fit properly.
- Always help a client to eat in the sitting position with the head bent slightly forward.
- Give food separately such as a forkful of potato followed by a helping of meat and so on.
- Try to avoid mixing different consistencies of food e.g. chewy meat and mashed potato, this can cause choking as separate chewing and swallowing actions often take place.
- Make food moist to help with swallowing.
- Watch when giving drinks like fruit juice, water and tea, give only small amounts at a time and wait until you are sure each mouthful has been swallowed before giving another. Some clients may prefer to have small sips of fluid in between mouthfuls of food whereas others may prefer the whole meal to be followed by a drink. Think about the temperature of the drink.
- Never force food into a client's mouth if they have indicated that they do not wish to have any more.
- Get used to clients' ways by asking questions about what they like and do not like, observing their facial expressions and movements.
- Blind or partially sighted clients may cope normally with food if it is arranged on the plate in a special way explained to them as the hands of the clock, e.g. meat is at '12 o'clock', potatoes at '4 o'clock' and vegetables at '9 o'clock'. Remember to say where you have placed a drink and a napkin.

  Liquid level indicators can be attached to cups or mugs to bleep when the desired level of fluid such as tea has been poured in.
- Plate guards can be attached to plates to stop food being pushed off the plate and make it easier to get food onto the spoon or fork.
- Many clients can be fully independent with feeding themselves if the food is cut up into small pieces and special cutlery with easy to grip handles are used with a plate guard.

Student activity 2

• In pairs, with one person in turn blindfolded, practise eating your lunch or tea with the least physical assistance. Imagine the difficulty if you were walking into a dining room you had never been able to see. How would you assist someone to get through the doorway in single file, find a table, eat a meal and go to the toilet afterwards?

DRESSING

When helping clients to dress or undress, a little bit of planning may save a lot of time later. If the client is able to say which clothes they prefer to wear then you are unlikely to have any difficulty getting the clothes accepted. If some items of clothing are unsuitable for the season try adding layers in winter or omitting under layers in summer but let the client choose. Remember, you may not experience the weather in the same way as an older or more restricted person. Activity generates heat to keep us warm and younger people tend to have more fat under the skin than an older person which alters the amount of body heat we gain or lose.

Not only do we put on clothing for privacy, feeling good, warmth and protection, but we use our clothing to express our personal identity. Once again, being observant and knowing your client helps you tremendously as you are likely to indicate the types of garments your client likes to wear. Remember to take account of cultural and religious modes of dress as well as whether the client can cope with the fastenings on the clothing, the size and the style.

Lay the clothes out in the order in which they need to be put on together with any aids which will help the client to do it on their own. Confused or elderly clients often mistake the order in which clothes should be put on.

There are many ways in which dressing can be made easier for clients who are elderly or restricted in their movements. Buttons can be replaced by touch and close tape, devices on a stick to hold stockings and tights open so that the client does not have to bend. Some ladies might prefer trousers or warm track suits and socks doing away with the need for stockings etc., others would never dream of wearing such garments.

Shoes are worthy of special mention. Elderly clients should be encouraged to wear proper shoes, rather than slippers or soft moccasins, for a while each day. Feet not used to shoes flop about and quickly get unused to support, which then causes pain when shoes are worn, so setting up a vicious circle. Many people may need specially fitting for shoes or shoes may need to be adapted, e.g. with touch and close fastenings.

When helping people to dress with restricted movement in one limb such as after a stroke, place that limb into the clothing first as the other can bend and thus be more flexible to place in the other half. While undressing, remove the good limb first and slide the clothing off the affected side. Think how you would do it to minimise your own pain if you had an injured arm or leg.

BATHING

Not everyone can be bathed at the same time of day in residential accommodation, so bathing often makes people appear difficult or resentful if the time given does not suit them. Take a little time and trouble to help clients find an acceptable time, but even then slavishly following a timetable should be avoided, if an individual does not feel like a bath, it should not be forced. Bathing should be a calming, relaxing experience, the client should be encouraged to do as much as possible for themselves to maintain their own privacy and dignity. Everything should be ready at the beginning of the bath as no-one likes waiting while wet for something to be found and it can be highly dangerous to leave a dependent client on their own while something forgotten is fetched.

Bathroom safety precautions should be observed such as non-slip mats, safety rails, dry, clean floors and no electrical equipment etc.

With everything ready and the bathroom door closed, help the client to undress making sure their clothes they will wear after the bath are ready. Check the temperature and depth of bath water with the client and double check these are correct before the client enters the bath. Use the toiletries the client wishes and ensure that the client's body is washed all over. Most people appreciate their back being washed. Allow plenty of time, both for the bath and dressing, allowing the client to do as much as possible. While the client is busy, you can be busy tidying and cleaning the bathroom while chatting to them. Many problems come to light in the intimate warmth of a bathroom, but take care with confidential information.

Warm towels and help with drying are usually appreciated, but too vigorous rubbing should be avoided if the skin is thin and wrinkled. Pay particular attention to crevices where the skin folds. Such areas are under the breasts, between the thighs and toes. Cutting nails is much easier after a bath as they are softer, but many clients might require the expert help of a chiropodist.

Some clients prefer showers, others hate them – people should be allowed free choice. Showers are safer for clients provided that there is good temperature control, use of non-slip mats and provision made for drying the floor after each shower. It is more difficult for helpers to assist clients with washing in the small confines of a shower cubicle, unless they wear swimsuits.

There are many aids to assist with bathing and many specially adapted baths, but, here we have just been concerned with the actual process.

SAFE LIFTING TECHNIQUES

In some care establishments, unpaid volunteers, particularly young people, are not allowed to lift clients. This is to protect the volunteer and the client from personal injury and to meet the insurance requirements.

In your GNVQ evidence, you are required to describe safe lifting techniques in accordance with European Union regulations and for carrying objects and people. This does not mean that you have to lift clients to achieve competence, although many health and social care students may lift in other activities. Clients can be difficult to lift because they are often heavier than you, awkward to get hold of and unpredictable. This means that they can make unexpected noises, movements, resist a lift that is going well and so on.

It is important for your own protection that you are taught correctly and expertly supervised during any demonstration. You should not learn to lift from reading a book.

Books will help you revise correct ways, but you should be properly trained by an expert before being allowed to lift.

In 1993, the European Union (EU) introduced new regulations for manual lifting which update an existing law called the Health and Safety at Work Act. This new law means that both the employee and employer have responsibilities for safe practice while lifting and moving clients. It is sometimes difficult to tell the exact difference between skills and procedures, you may know the procedure for lifting but be unable to carry out the lift. This can be a dangerous situation because you may in fact, be skilled in unsafe practice. The carrying out of safe lifting is a skill which requires practice and coaching by an experienced trainer, who has the ability to notice and correct any faults you may have. The following is a summary of the new law.

Responsibilities of employers

- Provide satisfactory training at start of job and annually.
- Record all training.
- Develop a code of practice.
- Supply and use mechanical lifting aids.
- Assess and reduce risks in lifting.
- Record risk assessment.

Responsibilities of employees

- Take reasonable care of own safety.
- Take reasonable care for others' safety.
- Use the code of practice.
- Report any risks in lifting.

Remember, never lift a client if you are not allowed to do so and if you have not been trained by an expert.

Ground rules of lifting

 • Stop. Think.

- Assess the lift. Can the client help themselves? Are mechanical aids available? Is there enough space? How many lifters are involved? Is suitable clothing and footwear being worn?
- Plan the lift. What is going to happen? Does everyone (including the client) know what is happening? Who will act as leader and give the instructions?
- Carry out the lift. Points to remember – all lifters should work together, everyone should wear suitable clothing (trousers are preferable) and flat shoes, and remove jewellery, badges and watches. The area should be free from obstructions. Take time to perform the lift correctly, never lift with a twisted back, make sure you keep balanced where possible, avoid stooping. Tuck your chin in, get as close to load or client as possible, never lift with arms stretched out. Always start with both legs bent at the knees, use power of your strong leg and buttock muscles in straightening and so lifting the load. Never drag or pull a client. Make sure all brakes are on if dealing with movable equipment.

Your trainer will tell you the different types of lift, they must not be practised from following pictures in a book. The trainer will watch you and give you feedback on your performance.

You will need to know how to assist a client from a lying to a sitting position, move from a bed to a chair and back again, assist to and from a wheelchair and to the toilet.

Apart from the care setting, you may also be required to lift a heavy load. The same principles of lifting also apply in this situation.

- Think about the lift, inspect the object and the area involved in the carrying – make sure there are no obstructions in the way.
- Get others to help if you can. Decide how the object is to be held and positioned.
- Stand close with feet apart. Move as close as possible to the object, having one foot either side if possible. Keeping the back straight, bend the legs at the knees.
- Get hold of the object firmly, breathe in and slowly straighten the legs until they are straight.
- Keeping the item close to the body, lift smoothly and if necessary take small steps to the new position. If you need to turn, move your feet, never twist your back when carrying a load.

Student activity 3

 • Describe what you know to be the important rules when lifting an object and a client.
- Observe and record a care assistant carrying out a lift. Make your own informal assessment.

MAINTAINING CLIENT INDEPENDENCE AND DIGNITY

Several times through this chapter, we have made statements such as

- allow the client to do as much as possible for themselves

- let the client choose
- maintain the client's privacy

Let us now examine independence and dignity a little more.

If you make assumptions about clients then you are prejudiced. If you make assumptions about what other people want to do, say, wear, eat, sit, etc. you are imposing your will on them and taking away their identity, self-confidence, independence and choice. When you are there to give physical assistance, you are there to offer help only if it is required by the client. Listen to what a client has to say, observe their facial expression, body posture, gestures and movements to find out their wishes. Ask, communicate, use gestures and body language yourself to give them as much choice as possible – and respect the answer.

Some carers will ask clients their wishes, but if the answer is not the expected one or the convenient one, then ignore the response or pressurise the client to agree to an alternative. Negotiation can take place, that is part of everyday life, but the client should be able to compromise or not, for themselves. Clients should be offered respect, even though they may be difficult at times. We all have our good and bad days, our moods and degrees of cooperation. The pleasant client has a right to be different if something has upset them.

Many clients might find it difficult to join in certain social activities, but the carer must not decline to invite that client or turn down an invitation on their behalf without asking first. Clients with disabilities must not be labelled 'the rheumatoid arthritis in the second bed on the left', 'grumpy' has eaten his breakfast this morning and so on. In fact, clients should be given their correct name and title unless permission has been given to call clients by their first names. Carers must recognise that they cannot solve all their clients' problems, in fact they probably solve very few, but more often support clients in ways which help them work through their difficulties and suggest solutions for themselves.

Carers, then, must accept clients for being the way they are, at any particular time on any particular day. They must not judge the way they are, not compare them or expect them to be like other clients. If we are to develop good caring skills to support clients we must show

warmth,
understanding
and sincerity.

This is done by being sensitive to clients' needs, treating them as whole human beings, using communication skills to convey acceptance, allowing them to retain and develop their personalities, giving personal choice whenever possible and trying to put ourselves in their shoes, to share their feelings and experiences as much as possible.

Clients should be involved in as much of their care as is practicable and results of medical examinations, outpatient visits and similar events should be discussed with them in private. If a client discusses something in private with you, it should be treated as confidential and not discussed with anyone else or recorded in notes. Confidentiality is the right of every client whether the information is written, verbal or recorded on computer. If the information puts either the client or some other person in danger, then you have the right to say to the client that you must inform your line manager. You have reached the limit of your confidentiality.

When do clients need physical assistance?

Observation of movement is important, if a client is clearly trying to carry out a task and movements are repeated several times unsuccessfully, then a tactful offer of help can be made. Do not be offended if the offer is turned down. You should be pleased that the client shows determination, perseverance and the independent spirit you are trying to encourage.

A client who is tense and anxious can show this by clenched fists, white knuckles, clenched jaw, hunched shoulders. Someone who does not want to talk to you can be partly turned away bodily or facially and have their arms or legs folded. They may wave you away with their hands or shake their heads if they do not wish you to carry on. A client sitting with head down or held in their hands is often depressed, sad, in pain or feeling hopeless.

The face is often said to mirror the emotions, very few of us can be distressed and not let it show on our face.

 Facial expressions give us clues about how a person is feeling

- frown – puzzlement, anger
- eyebrows raised – surprise, horror, questioning
- mouth with corners turned down – disapproval, depression, sarcasm, disbelieving
- mouth with corners turned up – joy, contentment
- lip biting – nervousness, worry

You will be able to think of many more.

If you need to ask a client questions to find out their wishes, try to ask open questions which begin with how ..., when ..., where . . . etc. and allow the client to answer as fully as they wish. Using open questions will enable you to collect a lot of information without repeating questions. Closed questions usually can be answered with one-word answers. To open the question, instead of asking 'what is your name?' you could say to a new client, 'how would you like to be called?' That should produce more opportunity for discussion. You might receive the response such as 'my name is Florence Wrighton, most people call me Mrs Wrighton but, as this will be my home from now on, I would be happy to be called Flo'.

Student activity 4

 • In pairs, role play a new client and a care assistant and then exchange roles to be a new care assistant with a long-term client in residential accommodation. Using open questions, practise obtaining as much

information about the likes and dislikes of the client in eight minutes.
• After each role play both discuss what it felt like to be that person for a few minutes and imagine a long-term residence with fairly regular exchange of care staff.

Take care not to 'grill' people by asking questions one after the other, it can be extremely tiring, use your powers of observation more and plan to obtain more information over the next few days.

Student activity 5

• Trying to use the sources of information in activity 1 in this chapter, explain how you or the carer would recognise when each client needed assistance.
• How would you give that help while maintaining each client's independence and dignity.

ELEMENT 8.2

Investigate the use of physical care aids

At the end of this section you should have

• described the main physical care aids and provided examples
• identified physical care aids to meet clients' needs

• identified ways of operating the aids
• identified key health and safety factors
• described constraints on the use of physical care aids.

MAIN TYPES OF AIDS

Aids for motor skills

These are aids which help people to things

which they might be unable to do at all, or find very difficult. The jobs are often frustrating and cause pain to some people.

These aids help clients with restricted motor skills or put more simply, people whose muscles and joints do not work as well as they should. Clients with restricted motor skills might have arthritis or have had a stroke.

Equipment for use in the kitchen might include kitchen tools with a good grip, extra large handles made of soft grip non-slip rubber, such as potato peelers, can openers, scissors. There are special holding tools because it is very difficult to grate cheese, butter bread, cut vegetables and carry out many other kitchen tasks if you only use one hand. Try it yourself next time you are in the kitchen preparing food.

Knives can be obtained with specially angled blades and easy to hold handles. They are for people who have very little strength in their hands and wrists.

Tipping equipment for kettles and teapots also help clients use them more easily and safely. Taps can be very difficult to turn if you have arthritis or weak wrists and long levers attached to taps make life much easier.

There are aids to help people dress themselves, keeping independence and dignity. Long-handled tools reduce the need for bending and lifting of the arms. Combs, shoe horns, bath sponges, gripping devices are all available on extended handles. A useful device for pulling clothes over shoulders is a long stick with a simple hook on the end. Button fasteners are available but many people replace buttons and zips with touch and close tape, much easier for arthritic people and elderly people to manage. Elastic shoe laces give the appearance of neatly fastened shoes while enjoying the simplicity of slip on shoes.

Socks, stockings and tights are all difficult to manage for people with reduced motor skills. Tights are particularly awkward because two legs have to be controlled at the same time! Simple but very effective devices are around to help with these, the socks are put on to the flexible plastic 'arms' and lowered on long handles to the feet, the foot is placed inside the arms and the sock is slowly pulled upwards over the feet by the arms.

Toothpaste dispensers do away with the need for squeezing toothpaste tubes and normal electric plugs come with stout handles for pulling out of sockets. Sockets are best relocated higher up on walls than at ground level.

There are also aids to assist people with leisure pursuits, such as a page turner for reading, needle threaders for hand and machine sewing and playing card holders and shufflers. Many people who find it difficult to use pen or pencil can operate either a typewriter or computer much more easily, either unadapted or specially adapted. A client with severe motor skills can use a computer with breaths from the mouth for example. There are now several best sellers written by severely disabled clients.

Aids for mobility

These are aids to help people unable to get around using their legs or can only do so for short periods of time or with great difficulty. The simplest aid with which we are all familiar is the walking stick. The best varieties, a little more expensive than those bought in an ordinary shop have large handles to fit the hand. Some types have wide specially shaped handles to allow the weight of the hand to be spread evenly over the handle. Others come in designs capable of being folded.

Giving yet more support are walking frames. Various types exist, some have wheels and some can be folded to fit neatly into a car. Walking frames can have bags attached so that shopping, books, knitting and money can be carried.

Figure 49   *Aids for motor skills*

Some frames can be awkward to direct around corners or take outside, three- or four-wheeled walkers fitted with brakes are, however, very flexible. Some types have seats attached so that when the journey is tiring, the client can rest for a while.

The aids mentioned so far have been for people with some mobility, for those with very little, there is the familiar wheelchair. Most have large rear and small front wheels and fitted brakes. People undertaking sporting events have specially adapted lightweight, easily manoeuvrable wheelchairs. Most wheelchairs are capable of being folded and have comfortable padded seats. To use a wheelchair to climb to a higher level, ramps are necessary and portable ramps are available. Wheelchairs cost several hundred pounds. The ultimate aid is of course a specially adapted car costing several thousand pounds.

Aids for transfer

This means equipment used for moving clients from one place to another, e.g. from bed to bath, from a chair to using a walking frame.

Costing several hundreds of pounds are powered bath lifts, and lever-operated bath lifts which raise and lower the seated client in the bath. Slightly less expensive is a turning bath seat – the client sits on the seat from the side of the bath and turns swinging the legs over the bath side. Simple seats which hang on the bath side are relatively inexpensive. (Remember baths are often slippery places, so anti-slip mats inside and outside the baths are a must for clients with restricted movement.) Grab rails and holding rails are important aids around baths, handbasins and toilets where clients need something to hold on to while carrying out their personal hygiene. Seats in showers are useful, particularly for frail elderly clients.

Toilet seats are often too low for many clients and raised toilet seats are much more convenient. Sprung toilet seats give assistance in lowering and getting off the toilet, exerting gentle pressure to help a client stand up. Toilet roll holders can often be out of reach of a client with restricted movement and simple carriers which fit on the outside rim of the toilet are more convenient.

Leverage stands help clients stand up from chairs and sofas that are too low, and electrically operated beds and chairs assist both clients and carers by saving muscular effort in lifting. Stairlifts help people to move up and down stairs and can be fitted both inside and outside the premises.

Both manual and electric hoists can be installed to transfer clients from one place to another and a simple swivel cushion placed on a car seat will enable clients to swing their legs to get in and out of a car.

Aids for feeding

Cutlery comes in many elegant designs and features thick non-slip plastic handles in straight and specially angled forms. The angled form means that the arm and wrist do not have to twist to get food into the mouth during eating. Wide two handled cups and mugs can be gripped securely and plates can be obtained with deep sides and raised rims to avoid spills. Bean bag lap trays mean clients can have a meal from a secure surface on their knees. Non-slip mats put under plates stop them from sliding about when a client is trying to eat.

Aids for sensory skills

VISUAL IMPAIRMENT

Books in large print or braille will enable a client with visual impairment to enjoy reading. Talking books are also important substitutes for reading. Magnifying glasses will assist a client to sew, knit or carry out similar leisure pursuits. Large print playing cards allow a client to participate in card games.

A guide dog is a living aid, allowing a client with severe visual loss increased mobility and companionship.

Clients with less severe visual loss should have spectacles produced to their own prescription by an ophthalmic optician. Large thick felt pens and a pad may help in communicating with some people with poor eyesight.

HEARING IMPAIRED CLIENTS

The most common aid is the hearing aid and most of us are familiar with clients who use them. Other aids are available.

- Headphones. Special devices for listening to the television.
- Induction loops. Wire loops set up around the room or building and people using hearing aids can pick up the electronic signals without also hearing background noise. Churches, cinemas, public halls often have induction loops.

- Programmes on television often have sub titles available from teletext television sets.
- Flashing lights on the telephone indicate when the phone is ringing.
- Amplified earpieces or fitted induction loops can make hearing the caller much clearer.
- Doorbells connected to flashing lights rather than bells.
- Alarm clocks which flash lights or vibrate under the mattress.
- Good lighting helps a hearing impaired client to lipread much more easily.

WAYS OF OPERATING THE AIDS

There are two main ways in which equipment is operated – manual and automatic. Manual operation is by the hand or other part of the body. Walking sticks and frames, typewriters, sock pullers are all examples of manually operated aids. Automatic aids are often powered by electricity, batteries or mains, powered lifts and hoists, electric wheelchairs are examples of these.

If you are caring for someone always make sure you know the right way to use equipment, either by asking an expert or reading carefully the manuals which are supplied with the equipment.

HEALTH AND SAFETY FACTORS

It has already been stated that you must know how to operate equipment correctly, if you are unsure you may cause an accident and this would distress both the client and yourself as well as probably resulting in injury to one or both of you.

Equipment must be kept in good repair. Any faults must immediately be reported to the appropriate authorities in verbal and written form. This will usually be your immediate supervisor. Serious faults mean that the equipment must be taken out of use, labelled as faulty and a replacement found. This is not always easy to do, but clients have a right to be safe.

CONSTRAINTS

For many clients, the cost of physical care aids prevents them obtaining them. Welfare services often cannot supply all clients' needs due to a limited budget, and the client, who is frequently on benefit, cannot afford to buy them privately. Other clients have not got space to store items like lifts and hoists, especially if they live in a flat with a family.

Access can also be a problem, stairlifts for example cannot be installed if the stairs are several short flights around corners, hallways and passages need to be wide enough for a wheelchair to turn round.

Student activity 6

 - Mr Edward Jones is 83 years of age and has recently suffered from a stroke. This left him with a right arm and leg which are much weaker than normal. He now has difficulty in dressing, feeding and walking. For the past five years, he has been progressively becoming deaf in both ears, he has done nothing about this, putting it down to old age.
- Describe Mr Jones' needs.
- Choose one manual and one automatic aid

and describe how each physical care aid you have chosen meets Mr Jones' needs, how each aid should be used in the correct health and safety manner and what constraints (restrictions) there could be in the use of each aid for Mr Jones and for other clients.

Investigate how aids help maintain independence

At the end of this section you should have

- identified and provided examples of the main sources of aids
- identified and provided examples of

support networks available to clients using aids
- explained ways in which physical care aids help maintain client independence.

SOURCES OF PHYSICAL CARE AIDS

Where can you get aids for use in physical care? In most communities in the UK, there are four main sources – National Health Service, social services, voluntary organisations and private organisations.

National Health Service

If the loss of motor skills, mobility or sensory impairment is part of an illness that means a client has been taken to hospital, then the hospital will supply equipment on a temporary basis. For example, a client with a fractured leg will be supplied with crutches, a client needing a wheelchair for transport within the hospital will have one provided. Occupational therapists will provide equipment for rehabilitation (this means helping a client resume daily living activities). Occupational therapists are professionals who are able to assess clients needs and provide aids to help with motor skills and mobility. Hospitals usually provide aids for clients who are visually and hearing impaired.

The general practitioner service, the client's doctor, can provide aids on a prescription basis.

The district nursing service can arrange for aids for differently abled clients, usually those associated with personal hygiene and being bed bound.

Social services

For clients in the community, the main source of aids in physical care is the social services. Many departments have their own community occupational therapy (COT) section, who assess needs and supply non-medical aids as required. There may be a cost involved, but some departments still arrange to supply them free of charge. Types of aids range from small items to help with feeding, such as cutlery, to large adaptations to a building, such as installing a stairlift. The client may have to pay part of the costs.

In some areas, because the range of aids is so large, the social services provide a type of showroom, where clients can select the aids most suitable to them. Leaflets providing information on the availability of aids to physical care are obtainable from the departments.

The Disabled Living Foundation run an information and referral service for clients and their carers. This is a free service based in London.

Voluntary organisations

These are charitable institutions which provide specialist support and information. They are not set up by local or health authorities and as a rule are able to be more adaptable in meeting clients' needs.

Examples of voluntary organisations are Age Concern, Talking Newspapers organisations, Association of Stroke clubs, Womens' Royal Voluntary Service (WRVS). You will be able to find many more examples both locally and nationally.

Private organisations

These are businesses, run for profit. You will find your local establishments in your commercial telephone directories. They are likely to be listed under 'suppliers of equipment for the disabled'. It is nearly always possible to obtain a catalogue of the types of equipment which they supply.

SUPPORT NETWORKS FOR CLIENTS USING PHYSICAL CARE AIDS

Networks to support clients needing aids are varied both in their nature and the support workers involved.

Self-help groups

As their name suggests these are groups made up of members with similar interests and difficulties in daily living. They share solutions to problems, enjoy social activities together, raise funds and support one another in all types of need. Most groups of this nature have sympathetic professionals available in case of need. Such groups are composed of clients, their families and other relatives. A committee is formed to make decisions and organise events.

Support groups

These groups may also have clients, their families and relatives among their membership, but many other people may be involved through interest or paid work. There are usually some paid workers in a large support group. They may carry out clerical duties, visit clients or be mainly concerned with providing accurate information. However, most of the helpers will be volunteers. This type of organisation will usually provide information and publicity leaflets, some of which will include how and where to obtain support and what physical care aids are available. This type of group includes Age Concern, Red Cross, Scope and Mencap.

There are local branches of most large support groups and you can see notices about meetings and other events in the local library, hospital (usually around the occupational therapy and physiotherapy departments) and public meeting halls.

There is a directory of voluntary care agencies in your area available from the public library.

Student activity 7

- Choose two clients who need different physical care aids. You might have a member of your family who has a hearing aid, a neighbour or fellow student who uses a wheelchair. You might, always with their permission, speak to someone from your placement, paid or unpaid work.
- Identify the physical care aids which are used and where they came from.
- Which support networks are available to each client?
- How do the aids help each client to keep their independence?

If you have extreme difficulty in finding clients you could use case studies for this assignment. There is one for you in Element 8.2.

9

INVESTIGATING HEALTH AND CARE SERVICE PROVISION

Investigate the organisation of health and care

At the end of this section, you should be able to

- identify the organisation of health and care services
- describe the main types of service available through each service provider
- describe the purpose of the main services

- describe how local health and care services are organised
- identify and give examples of the main local services
- identify and give examples of the main local services for which a client may have to pay.

ORGANISATION OF THE NATIONAL HEALTH SERVICE

This is not an easy thing to tell you about, as there always seem to be changes. The best thing to do is to find out how it works where you live. The student activity gives you some advice on how to go about it.

Student activity 1

- Arrange to visit your local community health council, or ask them if they have anyone who could come to your school or college to speak to the whole group

(you will find the address in the 'phone book).
- Ask them how the NHS is organised in your area.
- Who runs the hospitals, and how are they paid for?
- What is a health centre, and what do they do? Who pays for them?
- How do doctors, dentists, opticians and chemists fit into the NHS?

The NHS is an example of a 'statutory' organisation. This means that it was set up by the Government through an act of parliament. It is paid for by the taxes and National Insurance which everybody who works has to pay from their wages.

From 1 April 1996, there will be a central NHS office and eight regional offices in England. This means that there will be a Headquarters in London, and the rest of England will be divided into eight parts, each with a regional office, and smaller health authorities to look after the hospitals, doctors, dentists, etc. that you have found out about from the activity above. Wales has an office called the Welsh Office, which is the headquarters, and then Wales is split into five regions.

Northern Ireland has its own Northern Ireland Office, and four Health and Social Services Boards which look after hospitals and social services.

The important thing to do is to find out how the NHS works where you live. It is a national service, which is to say that the same service is available to anyone in the nation. Part of the service is made available through local hospitals, which can be found in every town. All the common illnesses and accidents are treated there. If a person needs more specialised treatment, such as for burns or for a head injury, there are regional centres they can be sent to.

Other parts of the NHS are the family doctors, dentists, opticians and pharmacists. It is the local health authorities who organise these. The family doctors (GPs) are the main part of the provision. They work from health centres and from surgeries. Most of the work they do is for the NHS, and is free to patients. Some of the services they provide have to be paid for if they are not fully covered by the NHS. If you need a medical exam for a job, you have to pay. If you have private health insurance and want to make a claim, the doctor will charge for sending them a sick note or a letter. Most things you see a GP about will be free, though.

You can have a private family doctor if you want, and you then have to pay them for any service which you get.

Health Centres have more staff in them than just the doctors. As well as indirect care staff such as the receptionists, secretaries and domestics, there may be nurses, physiotherapists, midwives and health visitors. Services from the other providers (dentists, opticians and chemists) all have to be paid for. Dental checks and eye tests all have to be paid for, and any prescriptions the doctor or dentist writes for you have to be paid for at the chemist. Some people can claim the money back from the Department of Social Security, but not everyone. All of these services also come into the private sector. Chemists and opticians are businesses that you buy things from. Dentists usually have just as many private patients as they do NHS patients.

SOCIAL SERVICES

This is another example of a statutory organisation, like the NHS. Some of the money to pay for social services comes from Government taxes, and more comes from the local Council Tax. Social services departments (SSDs) are a part of local authority provision. That means the town or the country where you live runs them and pays for them. They work to different boundaries than the NHS (except in Northern Ireland), and the county SSDs have district offices in the bigger towns. In big cities such as Liverpool, Cardiff, Belfast and Birmingham, there are district offices a few miles apart all over the town.

The people who work there are mainly receptionists, office staff, social workers, occupational therapists and home helps (often called home care assistants). There are other types of staff which you may have learned about in other Elements of this course. Some of the services they have are social workers, home care assistants, and residential and day care provision for elderly people, people with disabilities, and children.

VOLUNTARY ORGANISATIONS

Voluntary organisations are also known as 'charities'. These organisations are not part of any governmental provision and are not allowed to make any profit. They do need money to be able to provide a service, though, and this comes from people or private companies giving them money. They may also get money from statutory organisations such as the social services.

There are two kinds of voluntary organisations, **national** and **local**. National voluntary organisations include the Samaritans, Childline, the NSPCC (National Society for the Prevention of Cruelty to Children), the WRVS (Womens Royal Voluntary Service) and many others. Some of these may have local offices, but they are still national organisations. Local charities are those which only give a service in one town or group of towns. Examples are hospital Leagues of Friends, which only help out at one hospital, and womens' refuges which run a hostel in one town only. Other voluntary organisations usually have the name of the town in their title, such as 'The Blackbury Old Peoples Club' or 'The Tyneton Disabled Childrens' Support Group'.

Many voluntary organisations are actually **support groups** for people with the same or similar problems. Gingerbread is a support group for people who have been bereaved, for example. Alcoholics Anonymous is a support group for people who have alcohol problems. Most of the disabilities that you can think of have a support group which is a voluntary organisation which people affected and their carers can get help from (Motor Neurone Disease Society, Association for Spina Bifida and Hydrocephalus, Haemophilia Society, etc.).

Student activity 2

- Find out about all the health and care voluntary organisations in the area around your school or college, or where you live. The local library should be able to help you do this.
- Make three lists, one of them for local organisations, another for national organisations which have local offices, and the third for national organisations which do not have a local office, but which can help in your area. These might include Childline and other telephone helplines which you can call from anywhere in the country.
- When you have found out which voluntary organisations there are near you, find out what they do.
- Which client group or groups do they cover?
- Are any of the staff paid wages?
- Are all the staff unpaid volunteers?
- How do clients get help from them?
- Is there anything that you could do to help any of them?
- Can you go to visit them? Or can they send someone to tell your class about what they do?

PRIVATE ORGANISATIONS

The system of health and care provision that we now have is called a 'mixed economy of care'. What that means is that care can be provided from different places, statutory, voluntary and private. The private organisations include the big health insurance providers such as BUPA (British United Provident Association) and PPP (Private Patients Plan). People have to pay every week or every month to be members. Then when they are ill, they can go to a private bed in the local hospital, or into a private hospital. You can find out if there are any private hospitals near you by looking in the *Yellow Pages* telephone directory under 'hospitals'. They are very expensive if you have to pay yourself and do not have any insurance. There are also private agencies which will arrange care for people in their own homes, if they are paid to do it.

If you want to buy some aspirin or some cough medicine, you can get them in shops such as chemists or in supermarkets. These are private organisations. Chiropodists do almost all of their work privately, looking after peoples' feet by visiting them at home, or by seeing them in surgeries.

ELEMENT 9.2

Investigate access to health and care services

At the end of this section you should have

- identified the needs of different client groups locally
- identified and given examples of methods of referral of clients to local health and care services
- described the restrictions to clients gaining access to local services
- identified ways to improve physical access to local facilities for clients.

The information you have in your portfolio from Chapter 2 will help you to identify the general needs of the client groups in the range for this unit (infants, children, adults, elders, and people with special needs).

Look again at the PIES information which you have from Chapter 2, you may be able to use some of it as evidence toward this Element. Go through the exercises again if you need to remind yourself what PIES is about.

LOCAL NEEDS

You will know the area around where you live or around your college or school better than anybody who writes books. Is there anything special about the area? Are there a lot of children around, or are there a lot of retirement bungalows and flats nearby? Is there a hostel for any people with special needs, such as blind people, people with learning or physical disabilities?

Student activity 3

- Make a note of the main client groups in your area, and what there is to suit their needs.
- Have a discussion about this in your class, and see if you can identify any groups with special needs in your area who should have things arranged for them which most people do not need.
- There are some facilities, though, that everybody needs, such as GPs, dentists and hospitals. Are there any other things that you could add here? Some of the information you got together for Chapter 3 may be helpful to look at again.
- There are also things that people of different age groups need.

- Children

  - What health and care services do the children in the area need? Think of them in different age groups.
    - What would a baby need?
  - What do infants up to five years old need?
  - What do children from five years old and older need?
  - Are there any services which children need and adults do not?
  - Where is the nearest children's hospital?
  - What services do they have which ordinary hospitals do not?
  - Looking at the kinds of jobs there are looking after children (from Chapter 3) may help you with this.

- Adults

  - Are there any services which adults need which children do not?
  - Find out what they are, and write about them for your portfolio.
  - Do women have different services to men? Remember that it is the women who need maternity services, and also that the anatomy and physiology of men and women is different, and so different things can go wrong.

- Elderly people

  - What are the services which elderly people need to have that younger people do not? Think about social services as well as the health services, and services which can be given at home (domiciliary services) as well as residential and day care services.
  - Are there many retirement homes or nursing homes in the area?

- People with special needs. This name is given to a few different groups of clients, as we have mentioned above. They may be physically disabled in some way, such as blind or deaf, or needing to use aids to help them move about. These include crutches, zimmer frames and wheelchairs. There are also people with learning difficulties who may need specialist health and social care.

  - What needs do they have, and what is there to meet their needs in your area?
  - Does your school or college have people with special needs attending?
  - If so, what do they go there for? Which needs are being met?

METHODS OF REFERRAL

A referral is when a health or social care agency is asked to help a client. There are three main ways that this can happen, a self referral, a specialist referral, and a third-party referral.

A self referral is when you ask for help for yourself. A specialist referral is when you go to see your doctor, or perhaps your dentist, or a chiropodist, and they think that you need help or treatment that they cannot give. They will send you to see a consultant who specialises in what is thought to be wrong with you. A third-party referral is the person who asks for help for another person.

Student activity 4

 Read the case studies below and decide which type of referral each one is.

- Mrs J. sees her neighbour fall in the garden, and calls an ambulance.
- Jon has stomach ache and so goes to the doctor for help.
- Rachel cuts her hand at work and goes to the casualty department for urgent treatment.
- Jon's doctor thinks it may be appendicitis, so sends him to the hospital to see a surgeon.
- Chris goes to the dentist, and is sent to her GP because the dentist thinks the main problem is nothing to do with her teeth.
- Alan has an eye test and the optician sends him to the GP as he thinks there may be an eye infection which needs treatment.
- Sue is worried that her sister-in-law's children are not being looked after properly, so she rings the social services to tell them about it.
- Ram wants his house changed so that he can get around it better in his wheelchair. He rings the occupational therapist at social services for an assessment.
- The social worker thinks that Mollie is mentally ill, so asks a psychiatrist to visit and give an opinion.
- The health visitor wants to arrange care for a child when mother is in hospital having another baby. She rings social services for help.

See Appendix for answers.

RESTRICTIONS

Time

There are some health and care services which people cannot get by self referral, they have to go through a specialist. When they want to see a consultant, patients will first have to go and see their doctor and get a referral from there. If they can afford to pay, they can make a self-referral, but most people still go through their GP. For something urgent, it is sometimes possible to go to a casualty department and be seen there by a consultant without going to the GP first.

When a patient wants to see a GP, they will first need to know when the surgery or health centre is open. They will then have to make an appointment. It is not often that people can walk into a doctor's surgery and be seen quickly these days. So there are restrictions on when people can be seen, and sometimes by whom. In the bigger health centres, it is often the next doctor who is available that has to be seen.

Some casualty departments are open 24 hours a day, some close at nights, and occasionally at weekends. Other services are restricted in the times that they are open, and in the times that they are available to the public. Dentists and opticians work on an appointment system, and so do many social services offices.

Student activity 5

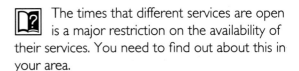 The times that different services are open is a major restriction on the availability of their services. You need to find out about this in your area.

- Is the casualty department open all the time?

- What system do the local doctors use? Do they all use the same system for appointments or seeing people at home?
- Do people have to make an appointment to see a duty social worker?
- Can people get an eye test any time they want one?
- How long do people have to wait to see a dentist?

Location

Student activity 6

- How far away are all these services to where people live? Do a survey in your school or college.
- Ask people how far they would have to travel to get to the casualty department or the social services office.
- Find out how much it would cost them in bus or train fares or by taxi.

If people live in the countryside, they could be a long way from any of the health and care services which are fairly easy to reach in towns. They would have to pay a lot more to get there.

Physical access

Remember that many of the people needing health and care services have trouble getting out and about.

Student activity 7

- What is the entrance like at the doctors surgery or the health centre?
- What about the social services office? Could people with wheelchairs or children in pushchairs get inside easily? Are there any double doors, swing doors, or sharp corners to get round. The biggest restriction will be if there are steps there, or if the office people want to get to is upstairs and there is no lift,

or the lift is not big enough or has other problems for disabled people.
- Are the floor numbers in braille as well as written?
- Can a person in a wheelchair reach the controls.
- Is the lift big enough to take a wheelchair and helper?
- Start by looking around your school or college. If you can borrow a wheelchair, so much the better. Make a tour and see where the problem areas are for wheelchair users, or other people who have difficulty walking.
- Draw a plan of the building you are touring and mark on it the difficult areas.
- How easy is it to get into the toilets (and out again)?
- Is the lighting OK for people with poor eyesight?
- When you have looked at the school or college, you will have a better idea of what is needed. Go and look at the offices of the health and care services in your area, including the voluntary organisations, and see what you think of their facilities for disabled people.
- If you had to put a ramp in to get wheelchairs in and out, what angle would be the best? If it is too steep, the user may not be strong enough to get up it, if it is too shallow, it would have to be longer and there may not be room to build it. Work the angle out for yourself and put it into your portfolio.
- Choose one of the services you have looked at, and write about how access could be improved. Remember that improving access for wheelchairs also improves access for mothers with children in prams and pushchairs.

Financial

Student activity 8

- Do any of the services you have been looking at make a charge to the patient or clients? Find out how much it costs to see a doctor, get a check-up from a dentist, have an eye test and see a social worker.
- You looked earlier at how much it costs for people to get to the various health and care services: This may put them off from using them. If they also have to pay for the service offered, that may put them off even more. Do a survey to find out how many people you know who do not bother going to the dentist, or who do not have an eye test because it costs money?
- The government also tries to save money by having specialist services in one place, and making people travel to them. We mentioned children's hospitals earlier. Find out where people from your area have to go for kidney dialysis. Where are the nearest burns unit, premature baby unit and psychiatric department? Not all hospitals have all of these.

EVIDENCE INDICATORS

Student activity 9

- What you will need to do for your portfolio evidence is find two people who live locally and receive help from the health and social care services. Find out how they were referred for help, whether they have to pay for any of it, and if they can get into the health and care buildings with no problem. You can use the work you did about access to buildings as evidence for the third part of the portfolio requirement.

ELEMENT 9.3

Investigate communicating information in health and social care

At the end of this section, you should be able to

- identify and give examples of the main sources of information about local health and care services
- identify and give examples of ways of publicising local services
- describe and give examples of the methods used to communicate information about local services to clients
- identify clients who may need adaptations in communication methods
- identify and give examples of ways of adapting communication methods to meet client needs for information about local services.

SOURCES OF INFORMATION

Libraries

When you are looking for information about health and care services, where do you go? Now that you are on a GNVQ course, you will probably start with the college or school library. That gives us a clue. If you are not on a GNVQ course, you could still start with the library – the local one for your town. You do not have to visit, you can 'phone up and ask for information as well. The staff in the library may not have the answers, but they should at least be able to tell you who is the right person to ask.

If you visit the library, you could look for information yourself in the reference section. Examples of books to look for are the *Social Services Year Book*, the *NHS Year Book*, and the *Charities Digest*.

Telephone directories

Something you may have in your own home or be very easy to get hold of are the telephone directories. If you know what you are looking for, then the ordinary directory is fine. If you do not know what you are looking for, but only the service, such as 'nurse' or 'wheelchairs', then you are best trying the *Yellow Pages* or *Thomsons' Directories*.

Citizens Advice Bureau

There is a Citizens Advice Bureau (or CAB) shop or office in most towns and some villages. They may not be open all the time, but only a day or two, or an evening or two a week. They are a voluntary organisation, and most of the people working there are volunteers. Some of the bosses are paid, but not many of them. They are there to give people advice and guidance on just about anything and everything, including health and social care matters – and they do it for nothing.

They have a good stock of leaflets, and an adviser that you can ask if you cannot find what you want, or need more detailed or personal advice. You will find the address of the one nearest to you in the 'phone book or from the library.

Post offices

Do you remember looking at rows of leaflets when you have been waiting in the post office? A lot of these contain information about the social security benefits people are entitled to if they are out of work, pregnant, or if someone in the family has died. There may also be information on other things, such as private health plans, or local voluntary organisations.

The best way to find out is to visit your local post office and collect a selection of what they have. Unlike the library, it is probably not a good place to ask the people behind the counter for information on health and care provision.

Health centres, doctors' surgeries, GPs

Health centres and doctors' surgeries are good sources of information about NHS services, health matters in general, and about some of the services from social services, and some of the benefits from the Social Security Benefits Agency. There is often a good selection of leaflets and posters around, some of them are about private provision, and where you can find the chemist, dentist, optician and chiropodists. The GPs themselves will be able to discuss health matters with you on an individual or group basis (have you tried inviting one in to speak to your class about the work they do?).

In health centres you are more likely to find other types of health and care staff, so you could get information from nurses, midwives and health visitors, for example.

Community Health Councils

There is a Community Health Council (or CHC) in every area of the country. Use the 'phone book or ask in the library where your nearest one is.

They are a part of the NHS which are there to help people in their dealings with the NHS. They give advice and guidance on how the NHS works, and help people gain access to services, or complain about poor services. They are also a very useful source of information on all health and some social care matters.

Social services offices

Social services offices are to be found in every area. If you visit them, there are often leaflets in the entrance area with information about social services and social security benefits. It is also possible to see or make an appointment to see an adviser or duty social worker.

This is the best place to find out about the personal social services, and residential services for children, elderly people, and people with disabilities. There will also be information on voluntary groups, and private provision for both residential and home care.

WAYS OF PUBLICISING

Look at the work you did for Chapter 3, Element 3 about job advertisements. That work will help you with this Element, too.

The media

The media is the name given to newspapers, magazines, cinema, television, radio and posters. When providers of services are looking at ways of publicising what they have to offer, they have to take into account what sort of people they need to inform, and how much it will cost. For national campaigns such as immunisation against measles, or to make people more aware of the dangers of smoking, then television advertisements, radio and national newspapers would be the best. The same would be true for a big private health organisation such as BUPA. For a local dentist or chiropodist, advertisements in the local paper or in the post office or other local shops is far cheaper, and will reach the people who will become the patients. Cinemas have national advertisements and local advertisements.

Student activity 10

- Design a poster for a baby-sitting service.
- Find out from a printers how much it would cost to have 100 printed.
- Decide where you are going to put it; think about who your customers are going to be. Where would be the best place to put advertisements that they will see?
- Find out how much it would cost to advertise in the *Daily Mirror*, or the *Sun* newspapers.
- How much is it to put the same

Figure 50   *Advertising can be effective*

advertisement into your local paper?
• What would your nearest cinema charge you
  to advertise on their screen?
• What is the cost of putting up posters in the
  post office?
• How else could you advertise?

The service itself

Specific health and care services advertise
themselves by having their names on the outside of buildings or on the sides of vans and
buses.

They sometimes send letters to every
household in a town, for instance the
NSPCC and Childrens' Society fundraising
campaigns.

If a service is particularly useful, everyone
knows about it by word of mouth, people
tell each other about it, for instance with the
Crossroads care attendant schemes, which
provide 'granny sitters' for carers of elderly
and sick people.

Health and care workers

Health and care workers themselves are a
good way of publicising a service. Many
health and care services will provide a speaker to groups of people such as colleges and
schools, clubs and factories.

Methods

ORAL

One way of publicising services is **oral**,
which means by the use of the human voice.
Health and care workers go out and tell people about what is going on. They could also
do this on national or local radio and this
would still be oral.

Audio tapes are another way and a way

that is particularly useful to people with a visual impairment, including blindness. It may also be on screens such as TV and video, and at the cinema, together with other types of information in graphical and statistical form.

GRAPHICAL

This is the use of pictures to get a message across, or make it easier for people to understand. Pictures are also very useful in getting information to people who cannot read, or who do not know the language. Think about road signs, which are the same in nearly all countries of the world these days.

STATISTICAL

Statistical information is when it is shown in lists of numbers, or on graphs or with pie charts.

Ways of adapting communication

This is covered under the headings above, but as a reminder, you need to think about the following.

- Where to put the publicity to get to the people you want to get it to. Leaflets in the health centre or doctors' surgery are fine for people who go to see the doctor,

but not for fit and healthy people.
- Posters in the post office will be seen by people who go to collect their pensions or family allowances, or even just to buy stamps or lottery tickets.
- Keep the language as simple as is needed for the people who will be reading it. Use pictures to make it more interesting, and to help people who cannot read or do not know the language. Where there are enough people who do not speak English, consider producing the information in the language required, both in written or oral form – this may be on an audio tape, remember.
- When the information is for people with a visual impairment, use large print or put it on to an audio tape.

Student activity 11

 • For the evidence in your portfolio, you may want to look at two local services, e.g. the social services and a private hospital, or a local voluntary organisation and a chiropodist.
- Go and find information about them both and write down where you got it from.
- Look at the types of publicity used and describe the methods of communication and if and how they meet the needs of the people they were prepared for.

APPENDIX

Answers to questions

C H A P T E R 2

Development questions

1   9 months
2   2½ yrs
3   2yrs
4   1 month
5   18 months
6   3yrs
7   1yr
8   2yrs
9   6 months
10   18 months

Development activity

1   (Active) old age
2   Young adult
3   Baby/infant
4   Toddler/infant
5   Elder/old age
6   Adolescent

Social influences exercise

1   A
2   b
3   c
4   a

Self check questions on education

1   4 or 5 yrs old
2   2yrs old
3   Afraid that mother will not come back
    Frightened of being left alone
4   Live there
    Sleep there
5   16 years old
6   Staying away from school without
    permission
7   Not being allowed to go to school
Questions 8, 9 and 10 are subjective

Relationship questions

1   A
2   C
3   B
4   B
5   A

Relationships

1   B
2   A
3   B
4   C
5   A
6   B

Answers to 'SPICE' questions

1 P
2 I
3 P
4 C S
5 S
6 E
7 E
8 I

Self check questions

1 User/service-user/patient/customer
2 Patients
3 Children, elders, people with special needs
4 A carer who is paid for doing the job
5 C
6 B
7 A
8 See the section headed 'Things you need to know'
9 D
10 Using good communication skills

CHAPTER 3

Self check questions on caring jobs

1 Look after the buildings, equipment and the direct care staff
2 Porters, domestic assistants, catering staff, administrative staff, etc.
3 Administrator, receptionist, clerical assistant, etc.
4 Plumber, electrician, engineer
5 Cooked meals delivered to people in their own homes
6 Catering staff, cooks
7 B – voluntary organisations
8 Ex-offenders
Recovering mentally ill
People with learning difficulties
Battered wives, etc.

Health care
Accident and emergency dept
Dentist
Health visitor
Doctor
Optician
Hospital
Nursing home
Midwives

Social care
Day nursery
Retirement home
Social worker
Home help
Playgroup
Social services dept
Children's home
Benefits agency

CHAPTER 9

1 Third party
2 self
3 self
4 specialist
5 specialist
6 specialist
7 Third party
8 self
9 Third party
10 specialist